HERBAL C

Create your own personalized beauty plan with this harvest of
natural herbal recipes.

2

HERBAL COSMETICS

Simple and Effective Natural Beauty Treatments

CAMILLA HEPPER

THORSONS PUBLISHING GROUP
Wellingborough, Northamptonshire

Rochester, Vermont

First published 1987

© CAMILLA HEPPER 1987

British Library Cataloguing in Publication Data

Hepper, Camilla
Herbal Cosmetics
1. Herbs   2. Cosmetics
I. Title
668'.55   RA778

ISBN 0-7225-0807-7

Printed and bound in Great Britain

CONTENTS

INTRODUCTION: TAKING HERBS INTO YOUR LIFE

There was a time when the search for beauty ignored the most important attribute of beauty – good health. A vital part of beauty is clear skin, shining hair, sound teeth and nails, and a slim figure.

The purpose of cosmetics should be to enhance natural assets, not to disguise them. The cosmetics themselves should improve the body, and not simply cover up its deficiencies. To do this it is necessary that what we put on our body should be natural ingredients. It is a sign of the times that commercial cosmetics are including more and more natural products, such as fruit, honey, vegetables and herbs.

Herbalism

Many herbs, flowers and fruits have soothing, healing and beautifying qualities. Modern Western medicine is firmly rooted in herbalism, and many commonplace drugs, such as aspirin, were originally derived from plant sources.

The uses and effects of herbs are well-documented. Any possible side-effects, after long-term use, are far more predictable than those caused by many synthetic products. Generally, herbs are very gentle in their actions. If you have a sensitive skin, herbal cosmetics do have a distinct advantage over commercial ones. Many skins are allergic to such substances as alcohol, aluminium salts and benzaldehyde, which are often used in commercial products.

Apart from these considerations, making up your own

cosmetics can be both fun and economical. Many of the ingredients, such as fruit, vegetables, yogurt and olive oil are already to hand. Most of the herbal ingredients can be bought very cheaply or, better still, grown at home.

Do-It-Yourself

When you make your own herbal products, they can be suited to your individual requirements. You know exactly what is in them, and how they were made. You will not be paying for famous brand-names and fancy packaging.

Begin by making up small, experimental batches with varying amounts of ingredients that you know are fresh. Keep careful records, so that you will be able to reproduce the mixture and strength that are most effective for you.

You will experience the satisfaction of being constructive and creative, from the growing and harvesting of herbs to the using of them, and the enjoyment of their long-term benefits to your health and apearance.

Another benefit of making your own herbal preparations is that you will be making a contribution to the fight against the use of animal products and the cruelty of animal testing. Many commercial cosmetics and household products are tested for safety on animals. Experiments include the introduction of irritating, inflaming or corrosive substances to animals, either by squirting them into their eyes, rubbing them onto bare skin, forcefeeding or injecting.

The LD 50 is an example. Single doses of substances are introduced into the bodies of small batches of animals. Should 50 per cent or more of them die, then the substance is rejected as dangerous to humans. Hence LD 50 – Lethal Dose 50 per cent. There are many campaigning organizations that will send you details of firms manufacturing household goods, etc., which do not involve cruelty to animals. None of the recipes and methods in this book involves animals in any suffering.

Equipment and Facilities

If you are fortunate you may have a room in your house where you can conduct your experiments without interruption. However, for most of us there must be compromise, and the next best thing is to have some space in your kitchen where you can work. Keep a separate set of those items you need for cosmetic preparations:

A couple of enamel saucepans – ordinary metal may taint some mixtures

A few bowls – preferably heatproof glass

A fine, nylon sieve for straining mixtures

Coffee filter-papers for straining off small particles where a very clear liquid is required. (Muslin is difficult to clean and needs sterilization.)

Wooden spoons – a couple at least

Wooden spatula

Rubber spatula

A set of metal measuring spoons (avoid aluminium)

A set of metal measuring cups (avoid aluminium)

A funnel

Clean glass jars and lids; glass bottles and lids

Plastic spray bottle (similar to those for misting house plants)

Mortar and pestle (try to get one with a wide base so that you can exert extra pressure)

Scales

A pipette for dropping small quantities of liquids

Plenty of kitchen paper – invaluable for wiping out jars and mopping up spills, and far more hygienic than tea-towels

A set of sticky labels to keep absolutely everything labelled (make sure you date everything you make)

A notebook to record your experiments. Note anything that is particularly successful, or anything to which you are allergic.

Keep addresses of suppliers handy, and note stocks that need renewing.

Keep a clear space in your refrigerator for storing your creams and lotions. Eventually you may find it a good idea to pick up a small second-hand fridge to store your products. The recipes in this book give small, sensible amounts which should be used within two or three days. To retard any deterioration, always use clean hands when you use the products; keep them away from fierce heat and strong sunlight; keep the caps and lids screwed on tight; place a layer of waxed paper over creams as you use them to keep the air from the surface.

Ingredients

Where recipes call for the use of vegetable oils, try to buy cold-pressed, unrefined oils. They usually have far better keeping qualities and retain more vitamins and trace elements than those that have been made 'pure' by chemical treatment. They may be a little more expensive than those bought straight from the supermarket shelf, but they are well worth it in terms of goodness. Ask at a health food store if you have any difficulty in obtaining them.

Try to avoid using mineral oils such as 'baby oil'. They are not at all sympathetic to human skin and are thought to have some adverse effects on our uptake of essential vitamins.

Many of the herbs, oils and other substances can be tracked down in health food stores, chemist shops and old-fashioned grocers. In areas with a large immigrant population, you may find shops which offer the sort of exotic and unusual stocks you would find difficult to track down anywhere else. As more and more people are coming back to herbs, shops are offering a better range than five or ten years ago and their staff are better informed.

Your library and local bookshop may be helpful with specialist information. The Yellow Pages directory will also tell you of any herbalist or herb growers in your area. If you cannot get the ingredients you need locally, there are addresses of suppliers at the end of this book.

Caution!

In the recipes given in this book, the herbs listed may be used quite safely. However, as you experiment more you may be given or come across recipes using herbs with which you are unfamiliar. If you are ever in any doubt about a herb's safety, particularly if you intend making mixtures to be taken internally, consult an expert first. Remember that many very powerful drugs (e.g. digitalis from foxgloves) are from plant sources. Do not make the mistake of equating 'natural' with 'absolutely safe'!

When you are making your herbal preparations always observe strict standards of hygiene. If possible, keep separate utensils for all your measuring, straining and weighing and make sure that storage jars are sterilized before use. Wash your hands before and after all preparations. Some mixtures have preservative qualities all their own, but to be safe make up only small quantities of any recipe and always store them in your refrigerator.

If you have a sensitive skin and find that you 'react' to conventional cosmetics, it is a good idea to patch-test any mixture which you think may give you problems. Anyone can be allergic to anything! Apply a small amount of the substance to the patch of fine skin on the inside of the elbow. Cover the patch with sticking plaster and leave for eight hours or overnight. (If you are allergic to sticking plaster, place the substance on a small pad of clean cotton wool and bind onto the skin with a strip of fabric of your choice.) If the substance leads to redness or soreness it is obviously causing a reaction. Keep notes of all your experiments; they are an invaluable source of reference and you will know which ingredients to avoid in future.

1. GROWING, HARVESTING AND PRESERVING HERBS

The best source for herbs is to grow as many as possible yourself, so that they can be used absolutely fresh. However, there are some that have to be obtained from suppliers because they are not native to this country. It is therefore, useful to know how to store and preserve herbs.

You will soon become fascinated by these plants, and may find you are keen to possess every kind of mint or every fragrance of scented geranium. Remember that many plants regarded as weeds, e.g. stinging nettles, have tremendously varied uses.

Below are a very few of the particularly useful herbs that you will use frequently. If you gather wayside plants and herbs, such as elderflowers or leaves, remember that those growing near busy roads are likely to be covered with dust and dirt. They are sure to be contaminated with lead. Pick well away from such areas.

Camomile (Matricaria chamomilla)
Annual. Low-growing, with small, white daisy-like flowers. Make certain that seeds or cuttings are definitely true camomile and not other members of the extensive *Matricaria* family. The plant contains azulere, and it has very good soothing and healing properties. The plants will set seed themselves or may be increased by root division in spring. Camomile is known as a 'plant doctor'. When planted or placed in its own pot near a sickly or poorly flourishing plant camomile will often help to revive it. As soon as improvement is noticed, remove the camomile.

Comfrey (Symphytum officinale)
One of the most useful of all the herbs. The plant grows up to
3 ft tall (60-90 cm) so place it at the back of borders. Sow seed
in early spring and thin the plants to 12 – 18 in (30-45 cm)
apart. It thrives in damp conditions. Because of its size it is
not suitable for container growth. Can be divided in spring
and, if roots are to be used, they are best dug in autumn.
Comfrey's active ingredient is 'allantoin' – a powerful healing
substance. Comfrey makes a good addition to the compost
heap where it promotes rapid decomposition.

Lavender (Lavandula spica)
A small, perennial shrub, growing 1-3 ft (30-90 cm) high. It
has blue, pink or white fragrant flowers. Dwarf varieties are
available. Can be grown from seed, but cuttings are more
usual. Follow instructions for stem cuttings (see p. 20). A
piece taken in summer should be rooted by late autumn, ready
for planting out in open ground in the spring. Attracts bees.
When dried it discourages moths! Trim to keep in shape.

Lemon Balm (Melissa officinalis)
A fragrant perennial, growing up to 2 ft (60 cm) high. It is
best grown from stem cuttings taken in spring or autumn and
set in a sunny position about 1 ft (30 cm) apart. It will grow in
most soils, though for strength of fragrance it prefers a moist,
rich soil. Cut it back to keep it compact. Attracts bees.

Marigold (Calendula officinalis)
Flowers are beautiful yellows, oranges and golds. It is very
easily grown from seed in spring in a light soil and sunny
position. Thin the seedlings to 18 in (45 cm) apart. They will
set seed year after year if left undisturbed. Cut off some of the
fading flowers to extend the flowering season.

Mint (Mentha)
There are numerous varieties of mint, including spearmint,
peppermint, applemint, gingermint and eau-de-cologne mint.
They tend to take quite a lot out of the soil and to be invasive.

They do better in damp and some shade. Put plenty of compost and manure into their soil, and preferably contain their growth by sinking roof slates into the ground around them, or plant them in a large bucket, sunk into the soil. Cuttings or bought plants are the most reliable.

Nasturtium (Tropaedum majus)
Beautiful trumpet-shaped flowers in golds, oranges and yellows. Attractive foliage. Sow seed in early summer in open ground or in pots. Ideal for hanging baskets, tubs, troughs, window-boxes etc. Produces more flowers on poor soil than on rich. Helps to protect other plants from pests.

Rosemary (Rosmarrius officinalis)
An evergreen shrub, usually quite hardy. It is slow growing but will reach 6 ft (2 m) in height. Dwarf varieties are available. It is strongly aromatic with needle-like leaves and small bluish flowers. Will survive in hot, poor soils. It needs lime and good drainage. Take cuttings in August and transplant in spring. Take 6 in (15 cm) sideshoots and put them into sandy compost where roots will develop.

Sage (Salvia officinalis)
An evergreen shrub 12-18 in (30-45 cm) high. It has a strong, savoury flavour. It prefers a well-drained sunny site. Grow from spring-sown seeds or cuttings taken in late spring and put straight into soil on new site, placing about 16 in (37 cm) apart. Pinch out growing tips, or cut back if plants become straggly.

Thyme (Thymus vulgaris)
Apart from the ordinary thyme, variegated and lemon-scented varieties are available. It contains a strong antiseptic – 'thymol'. Can be grown from spring-sown seeds, thinned to 12 in (30 cm) apart. Cuttings can be taken in spring. A dense, low-growing spreading plant, it is ideal for rockeries or even between paving stones.

Yarrow (Achillea millefolium)
A tall, hardy perennial, with dark, feathery foliage and
flat-topped clusters of white flowers. Can be bought from a
nursery as a hardy, herbaceous species. It helps other plants
to resist disease and enhances herb fragrances.

Indoor Culture

Most herbs can be grown indoors, though size is one of the
limiting factors. You need small, clean flowerpots, old saucers,
plates or plastic trays, clean gravel, garden compost or John
Innes No. 2 compost, sharp sand, a small, long-spouted
watering can, a water spray, liquid plant food, labels and
small planting tools.

A reasonable amount of light and space is needed for
successful results, and it may take some experimenting to get
the correct humidity. Aim for a group of herbs, perhaps
parsley, chives and thyme together, because plants usually do
better with some company rather than being grown in
isolation.

The best position is a sunny window-sill, preferably with a
sheer curtain to diffuse the light of the midday sun which can
scorch the plants. Old wooden trolleys from junk shops or
auctions or government surplus stores are useful. They can
take a number of plants on the top shelf, and be wheeled away
from the window if it is too hot, or to the kitchen for watering.

A good soil mix is about eight parts good garden compost to
two parts sand. Make sure that the pots can drain freely. Place
broken pieces of pot or small stones at the bottom of clay pots.
Plastic pots do not usually need any extra drainage material.
Stand the pots in saucers of gravel or together in trays of
gravel, which will help to drain excess water and regulate the
humidity around the plants.

Turn the pots occasionally so that light gets to all sides.
Mist the leaves and put the plants outside on warm days. This
is particularly beneficial if they spend a lot of time on a
kitchen window-sill where the leaves may get clogged with
dust. Leaves have to 'breathe'.

Avoid extremes of temperature in the room where the herbs are kept. Very sudden sharp rises and falls in temperature upset the plants. Protect them from draughts. The kindest way to water them is to fill a small, long-spouted watering can, and then leave it until the water reaches room temperature. Water is needed when the surface of the soil begins to look dry. It is always far easier to revive a plant that is thirsty than one which has been drowned. Overwatering can be disastrous. Do not leave flowerpots standing in water! Give an occasional feed with a liquid plant food – about every fourteen days. Too much food too often produces lots of lush growth but it may reduce the concentration of essential oils within the leaves.

The way to an instant indoor garden is to buy young plants in small pots. Good selections of herbs are becoming increasingly available from garden centres, or you may be lucky enough to live near to a specialist herb-grower. Look out for herbs at country fêtes during the summer or Women's Institute stalls in markets around the country.

Outdoor Culture

You need flowerpots, tubs, troughs, old sinks, light-weight plastic or polystyrene containers, good compost from your own compost heap or bought compost, soil-less compost for roof-top gardening, window-boxes or hanging baskets, peat, sand or manure to add to soil where necessary, labels, gardening tools and gloves.

You can grow a reasonable collection of herbs even in the smallest yard. Be careful about weight if you are planning anything for roof-tops or balconies – a small tub of wet soil can be heavy. Where weight is critical, use plastic and polystyrene containers filled with soil-less compost. Keep an eye on container-grown plants for signs of drying out. Those in terracota containers are particularly vulnerable.

Keep as many of your herbs as possible together near the house, so that you can pick them as you need them. But do not let this consideration stop you incorporating herbs into different areas of the garden: angelica, fennel, borage and comfrey make tall subjects for the back of a border; marigolds and nasturtiums give lovely golden sunny colour to any border; the thymes and marjorams are excellent in rockery settings, while the mints are ideal in shadier, damp places.

Herbs prefer an alkaline soil. If yours is acid you will need to add lime to it. If you do not know what sort of soil you have, you can get soil-testing kits from good gardening shops – or ask a knowledgeable neighbour. Heavy, sticky soil needs sand, peat and humus adding to it. Well-drained soil is essential because water-logged roots cannot 'breathe' and develop properly. Many herbs will tolerate a poor, light soil, but they all benefit from the addition of humus. Humus is decayed organic matter and provides plants with foods and minerals necessary to their health. It helps to improve the texture of the soil, keeping the roots moist without stifling them. In its best form, humus comes from well-rotted animal or vegetable compost.

If you have room, keep a couple of compost heaps in production. Use either bought compost bins or build your own with four stakes hammered well into the ground to make a 3 ft x 4 ft (1m x 1.3m) frame, and surround them with netting to a height of about 3 ft (1m).

Start with a layer of straw or bracken, add garden or kitchen waste (all vegetable and fruit peelings, tea-leaves, tea-bags, coffee grounds, egg shells, etc.), lawn mowings (but not if you have used weed killer or other chemicals on your grass), weeds (annuals only – before they set seed), leaves and other plant material. Avoid very tough evergreen leaves, very woody stems and sticks or thick cabbage stalks as these will not break down very quickly. Insects and bacteria will do all the decomposition for you, but if you are in a tearing hurry you can use a compost accelerator (the Soil Association has information on organic accelerators). Finish with a layer of soil and water your heap if it appears to be drying out.

If you cannot have a compost heap or bin, buy something

like hop manure to add humus to the soil. It is fairly expensive but does give good results.

Time spent preparing your soil is well worthwhile. Dig thoroughly before you do anything else. If you are not in a hurry let the frosts break it down over the winter. In spring apply an organic fertilizer in a thin layer, a mulch of garden compost and a little peat.

Let the soil settle for a couple of weeks before you begin planting. Plants can go into the soil at almost any time as long as there is no frost or snow. Choose potted herbs that are stocky and sturdy with a good firm network of roots which will probably be beginning to show through the bottom of the pot. Water the plants the night before planting. Dig a hole deep enough for the plant, invert the pot, and holding the fingers gently around the plant stem, give the bottom of the pot a sharp tap. The plant should slide out quite easily. Avoid disturbing the roots. Ease the plant into the hole and firm it in gently.

Then it is a matter of routine watering in dry weather and regular weeding. Do not overfeed with too many concentrated fertilizers, especially of the non-organic sort, or you may get too much growth but not enough active oils in the plants.

With plants that die back in the winter, label their sites so that you can leave them undisturbed.

Growing From Seed

When buying seeds make sure that they are fresh. Follow the instructions printed on the packet. Plant them when the soil is beginning to warm up in the spring. Cover lightly with soil and label, as some, like parsley, may take a very long time to germinate. When the seedlings have grown to about 2 in (5 cm) high or made four true leaves, thin them and transplant to their final sites.

To grow seeds indoors you will need seed trays, seed pans, seed compost (John Innes No. 1), labels, newspaper, sheets of glass, a mist-sprayer and John Innes No. 2 compost. Cover the drainage holes of trays or pans with pebbles or broken pots. Fill to within ½ in (1 cm) of the top with John Innes No. 1 compost. (Do not plant seeds in ordinary garden soil – its lack of sterility and the presence of weeds will not encourage good growth in the herbs.) Firm the compost, water and leave for several hours or overnight for it to warm up. Sow the seeds thinly, and then cover lightly with a thin layer of soil. Cover the trays with glass, place newspaper on top to keep out the light. If condensation begins to form under the glass, turn it over each day. Keep the trays at about 57°–60°F (15°C). When the seeds come through, remove the glass and paper and bring them into the light – but not direct sunlight. Mist spray the soil to keep it damp.

When the seedlings have four true leaves, transplant into John Innes No. 2, setting them 2 in (5 cm) apart. After a few days, 'hardening off' can begin by putting the small plants outside for increasingly long periods on warm days. After about twelve days plant them in their final growing positions, correctly spaced.

Increasing Your Stock

Layering
Many herbs such as sage, rosemary, mint, marjoram and lemon balm can be increased by layering. Choose a strong stem near the ground, make a slanted cut in the underside of the stem about 9 in (22 cm) away from the main stem. Put some rooting powder on the cut, bend the stem and bury the cut part firmly in the soil. Secure it with a small loop of plastic-covered wire. Leave for about six weeks until roots have formed. The stem can then be severed from the original plant, and the new herb carefully moved to its final site.

Stem Cuttings
Cuttings can be taken from healthy plants at any time during the growing season. Select sturdy stems about 4 in (10 cm) long with plenty of leaves and remove all the lower leaves. Fill

a seed pan or small flowerpot with John Innes No. 2 compost, dip the cuttings briefly into water, and then into rooting powder. Gently shake off excess powder and plant into the compost, setting the cutting firmly. Keep the soil moist and out of direct sunlight. Mints and thymes should root in about five weeks, but rosemary and lavender may take double that time.

Root Divisions
In autumn and early spring, when the plants are dormant, they may be carefully lifted and the root clump gently eased apart or cut. Replant the divided clumps immediately and water them well.

General Care of Plants
Apart from good preparation of the soil, attention to watering in dry weather, weeding and the application of a thin dressing of organic fertilizer in autumn or early spring, the plants need little further attention. Cut shrubbier herbs back by about half at the end of the growing season. This keeps them healthy and bushy. With softer stemmed perennials, cut right back, drying the leaves for winter use. You should have very little trouble with pests and disease if you maintain the correct conditions for the plants.

Problems usually arise with plants that are already weak and unhealthy. Some of the mints are affected by 'mint rust'. The shoots that come up in spring are twisted and covered with orange 'blisters', and then the leaves turn yellow and fall. Remove and burn these shoots. When the plants die back in the winter, put straw on the soil and set fire to it. This should kill all the rust spores in the soil. The disease does not affect the underground runners. To be on the safe side, take healthy cuttings the following spring and transplant to a new site.

Young seedlings may collapse at ground level. This is 'damping off' disease. It can be avoided by making sure seedlings have plenty of space, and that the soil is light and not liable to become waterlogged.

Harvesting and Preserving

Herbs vary as to the best time for harvesting. For best results pick them on a dry day, gathering in the morning after all traces of dew have gone, but before the sun's heat is too fierce. Herbs picked at the right time in the morning can have far more strength than if they are left to the end of the day. It is best to pick herbs when the flower buds have formed, but before the flowers open. Leaves have high concentrations of essential oils, but much of their strength is lost once seeds have formed. Try to pick only the tips of branches, and pick evenly to preserve the good shape of the plant. Remove any dead or diseased leaves.

Although it is possible to freeze many herbs, the simplest way of preserving and storing them for most uses is to dry them. Tie in small bunches and hang from the ceiling of a warm, dry room where the movement of air will dry them. When completely dry, wrap in tissue paper and put in a dark cupboard or drawer, or into jars and keep in the dark. They may also be dried by placing them in layers on trays, covered by a thin sheet of muslin and left for about twenty-four hours in an airing cupboard or other warm place out of direct sunlight. Do not put them in a low oven, as the colour and essences are all too easily lost. The main aim is to remove all moisture from the leaves and the stems.

Strip leaves from the branches and crumble them into jars, sealing well. Clear, glass jars should be kept in the dark – light causes deterioration in the herbs' 'strength'. With seeds, place them on a tray in a dry place, cover with paper for ten to fourteen days, and then store in jars.

Buying Dried Herbs

For herbs that you cannot grow yourself, try local delicatessens or health food stores. Find a supplier who keeps only a small stock, so that the dried herbs will not have been in the shop for several months or even years! There are also importers who supply by post. They often have a comprehensive catalogue and usually welcome your questions. Names and addresses are listed at the end of the book.

2. Hair Care

Hair is composed of a substance called keratin, which is similar in structure to the material of which our nails are made. The hair shaft is a hollow tube containing pigment which gives the hair its colour. The hair that is visible to us is 'dead' but it mirrors to a great extent what is happening inside and outside the body. Hair is kept glossy by the production of sebum in the area of the follicle, the baglike structure below the skin in which the hair rests. Healthy hair is maintained by a balanced diet and adequate exercise.

A few basic rules apply to all hair types:

When you wash your hair, have the water comfortably warm. Very cold or very hot water are too much of a shock to the scalp.

Wet the hair *thoroughly* before applying shampoo.

Use shampoo sparingly.

Rinse hair very thoroughly, until the water runs absolutely clear. A shower attachment makes this easier.

Pat the hair dry with the towel. Do not rub the hair or scalp hard.

Use a very wide-toothed comb to gently comb out the hair.

If you are using a hair dryer, hold it at least 4 in (10 cm) away from the hair. This applies particularly if you have it on a high temperature setting.

It is best to avoid the use of curling tongs and heated rollers. Use them in a dire emergency, but not every time you style your hair.

Avoid using chemical bleaches and dyes – the chemicals in commercial colourants can cause skin irritation in some people, and even result in dermatitis. There are good herbal alternatives. Too many perms involve the use of too many chemicals. As often as not, a good cut will do all that is needed for the body and shape of your hair.

Normal Hair

Normal hair has well-balanced sebaceous glands which provide just the right amount of sebum to lubricate the hair shaft. This type of hair normally stays clean-looking and the ends are resistant to splitting.

A good shampoo for normal, dark hair, can be made as follows: take 1 tablespoon rosemary and 1 tablespoon sage. Put them into a small bowl and pour on 4 fl oz (120 ml) boiling water. Leave to get cold, then strain. Meanwhile take 12 fl oz (360 ml) water, pour it into a saucepan and put in enough chopped leaves and stem of the soapwort plant so that they are just covered. Bring to the boil very gently, then let it simmer for five minutes. Leave to cool down, strain and add to the first herbal mixture. The rosemary and sage will help to keep the hair lustrous and dark. Soapwort has natural lathering and cleansing properties.

For blonde hair substitute camomile for rosemary and sage. For auburn hair use marigold or alkanet (a plant yielding a red dye).

Another good cleansing shampoo can be made by combining 1 fl oz (30 ml) olive oil, 1 fl oz (30 ml) castor oil and 6 fl oz (180 ml) water in which 4 tablespoonsful of a suitable herb (depending on hair colour) has been infused. (See section on 'Hair Colourants' at end of this chapter.)

If you want a dry shampoo you can apply powdered orris root to clean the hair. Comb the hair into sections, apply the orris powder at the roots, then comb it or brush it to the ends. Keep brushing the hair until all traces of the powder have been removed. This method of cleansing works a little better on fair hair than dark.

Another quick method is to take a small, clean piece of cheesecloth, soak it in lavender water or eau de cologne, wring it out and force the cloth over the bristles of the brush. Brush the hair thoroughly and the lavender water/eau de cologne will help to take away greasiness, dust and grime, leaving the hair far cleaner and smelling sweet. If your hair is very dirty you may need to remove the cloth, wring it out in clear water, reapply the lavender water/eau de cologne, wring out and reapply to the brush.

Dry Hair

This is a very common hair type and often benefits from external treatments as well as regulation of diet and general health, with plenty of protein, cereals, nuts, lean meat, fish, fresh fruit and vegetables. Bleaches, dyes, harsh perms, heated rollers, tongs, and backcombing can be devastating to dry hair. To the basic shampoo mixture for normal hair you can add or substitute infusions of elderflower, or mallow or comfrey root and leaf. All of these will help to improve the condition. Just by switching from the common detergent-based shampoo to gentle herbal preparations you will give dry hair a rest. Detergents tend to strip the hair of its natural oils, making it dull and brittle.

Scalp massage will also help to keep dry hair in better condition. Whenever you have a spare moment, press your finger tips against your scalp and rotate the scalp underneath them gently – the scalp has natural elasticity and movement in it. When brushing your hair, use a good quality bristle brush and bend forward from the waist so that the blood flows to your scalp. Brush the hair in long strokes, following and smoothing with the other hand. This helps to cut down any build-up of static electricity. Various conditioners are listed later which are good for dry hair.

Oily Hair

This hair type requires some patience in treatment because the correct balance has to be found. Some people find that too much washing sometimes makes the condition worse because the sebaceous glands become overstimulated. However, just leaving the hair and hoping that not washing it will right the condition often results in an unsightly mess of lank, stringy hair.

The best thing is to wash the hair as often as required, but to use a good, gentle shampoo. The soapwort-based basic shampoo for normal hair is excellent. For the herbal infusion part of the mixture use rosemary, lavender, lemon or yarrow. After shampooing, add 2 tablespoonsful of lemon juice or cider or wine vinegar to the final rinsing water.

You can keep ready-diluted vinegar in a large container ready for use. Dilute 1 pint (½ litre) of vinegar to 7 pints (4 litres) of water. A large plastic, screw-topped container is ideal. The vinegar smell soon evaporates and the hair should be shiny and soft.

Be gentle when drying your hair – mop out the excess water, and then dry naturally or gently with a hairdryer set to warm. When you brush your hair, do not scrape the scalp with the bristles of the brush – lean forward and brush gently so that oils are taken to the ends of the hair.

Watch your diet – eat plenty of fresh fruit and vegetables. Drink plenty of water to keep the body cleansed. You may like to try some of the mineral waters, many of which are available in grocery stores and supermarkets as well as health stores. Drink herb teas, too, particularly yarrow or horsetail tea. Some oily hair conditions are purely temporary – during puberty, and during and immediately after pregnancy – and the hair often goes back to normal very quickly.

Conditioners and Tonics

A very effective conditioner for *normal* and *dry* hair, especially if it is looking a bit lacklustre, is basically a mayonnaise. Don't try using the ready-bottled product though – it just isn't the same!

Take 1 egg, 6 teaspoons wine or cider vinegar, 2 teaspoons honey. Mix this together, then add olive oil, drop by drop, mixing continuously, until a thick, creamy mixture is obtained. (For best results use an egg at room temperature.)

Use the mixture before you wash your hair. Brush your hair out, then put the mayonnaise on, stroking it through to the ends. If possible take a plastic shower cap and cover the hair with it and wrap a towel, wrung out in hot water, round your head. The warmth from outside and your own body heat will help the conditioner do its work. Leave it on as long as possible, then wash out thoroughly with your favourite herbal shampoo mixture.

Coconut oil and peach-kernel oil also make excellent bases for conditioners for 'hungry' hair. You can substitute either of these oils for the olive oil, and combine them with egg, vinegar and honey in the same 'mayonnaise' mixture, and apply it in the same way.

If you want to massage oil alone into the scalp, wet the hair thoroughly with *comfortably* hot water. This will keep the hair shaft itself from being smothered in the oil, whilst opening the pores and making them more receptive to the oil. Keep the head warm, again with a shower cap and hot towels, for as long as possible before shampooing thoroughly.

For oily hair you will usually find that a gentle shampoo, herbal rinses of rosemary, lavender, yarrow, etc., and cider vinegar used in the final rinsing water will be very helpful. However, to give yourself a more substantial treatment, you need:

3 tablespoons of strong infusion of yarrow
3 tablespoons of rum
2 eggs separated (keep the whites)

Mix together the yarrow infusion, rum and egg yolks very

thoroughly. Comb your hair into manageable sections, and apply the mixture to the scalp with a pad of cotton wool which has been wrung out in water. Massage it into the scalp. Then pin that section out of the way and move on to the next section. Concentrate particularly on the oily areas around the front of the scalp, above the temples and the crown. Wring out a small, thin towel (or a thin gauze nappy) in a hot infusion of rosemary and wrap it around the hair. Put on a shower cap. You can put another warm towel or a piece of aluminium foil around the cap to maintain the heat. Keep the treatment pack on for as long as possible – at least an hour.

To shampoo the pack from your hair, beat the egg whites with juice from half a lemon until stiff. Use this frothy mixture to wash out your hair. Finally, rinse your hair thoroughly with cider vinegar in the water. This treatment gives the hair body and a very healthy sheen.

If you have long hair the ends may well be dry and split, even if your scalp is oily. Have the ends trimmed regularly and make sure that when you apply oil you hang your head down and brush your hair gently to distribute the oil evenly.

Hair Problems

Common problems like dandruff and falling hair can affect all of us at certain times. Both these conditions can be triggered by stress, changes in hormone balance (for example, during puberty, in and immediately after pregnancy, at the menopause) or illness. In some cases these problems become more of a chronic condition and may be caused by something in the metabolism of our bodies. In these instances it may be a good idea to consult a qualified medical herbalist who will be able to sort things out over a period of time. Generally, sensible diet and sensible living are enough to clear up these problems.

Dandruff
Dandruff causes enough problems and embarrassment just by showering clothes with little white flakes. It can also be

irritatingly itchy. If you find that modifications to diet and the use of home-made herbal preparations do not work, and you are suffering severe irritation with inflammation and bleeding, you should see a medical herbalist, a dermatologist or trichologist.

Most cases respond well to home treatment. Firstly, watch out for diet. Avoid excessively spicy foods, too much fat and sugar and very starchy white flour products. Cut down on alcohol as far as possible, particularly spirits. Take plenty of raw vegetables and fruits, vegetable oils and nuts, lean meat and fish.

Make up the basic shampoo mixture, based either on soapwort or olive oil/castor oil (both appear in the 'Normal Hair' section, p. 25), and add a strong infusion of nettles, nasturtium leaves, white willow bark or rosemary (or combine all of them). Rinse the hair with water containing cider vinegar.

All of the above-mentioned herbs have a beneficial effect on an unhealthy scalp. Combining these external applications with a good internal regime should give positive results quite quickly. If you are under stress, try out some of the ideas in Chapter 5. Remember to give your scalp a gentle finger-tip massage whenever you have the opportunity.

Falling Hair
This usually results from an illness, becoming 'run down' or a major hormonal upset. Everybody sheds hair every day of their lives, and each time you brush or comb your hair you will lose some. At certain times of year, like autumn, we shed more than usual, rather like a dog moulting. You may find that a course of brewer's yeast tablets taken at this time will help you through the transition. Again, check your diet and your hair-care habits, making sure that you are not using chemical-based colourants, dyes, perms etc. and that you are not using excessive heat from rollers, tongs or dryers. Wash your hair using either of the basic shampoo mixtures given at the beginning of the Normal Hair section adding an egg

beaten into the shampoo. Do *not* use water that is too hot or the egg will scramble. Leave it on for as long as possible. Use the mayonnaise type conditioner as often as possible. You may find that another dietary supplement, kelp, will help. Kelp is available in capsule form from most health stores. It is a form of seaweed, rich in vitamins and numerous minerals, and is beneficial not only to the hair but also to the skin and nails.

Setting Lotions

These are to help set hair, particularly if it has a natural tendency to be fine and rather limp. Vary basic setting lotions can be made from flat beer, lemon juice or sugar and water.

Lemon
This is especially good for greasy hair. Squeeze and strain juice from a lemon and comb it through the hair before setting on rollers. It leaves the hair feeling quite stiff when the rollers are removed, but once the hair is brushed out it feels and looks soft and silky. You can make a concentrated lemon preparation to spray onto the hair to keep it in place – far better than harsh hair sprays and lacquers. Cut a lemon into pieces and boil it with about a cup of water until the amount of liquid has reduced by half. Strain off the liquid, add a few drops of vodka to preserve it, and pour it into a spray bottle. Mist finely over the hair after styling. It dries quickly and keeps the hair in place.

Beer
This helps to give body to the hair. Simply wet the hair with it before winding onto rollers.

Sugar and water
This is a simple, old-fashioned method. Take a cup of boiling hot water, add a tablespoon of sugar, stir until dissolved and then use as required. Some can be stored in a spray bottle.

Hair Colourants

There are several ways of colouring hair using purely vegetable dyes. These are much kinder to the hair and scalp than many of the synthetic products and strong chemicals which can weaken and damage the hair. Do not use any of the following on chemically-treated hair until the chemicals have dispersed.

For Fair Hair
Camomile is excellent for bringing out blonde highlights. For a gentle lightening effect over a long period of time, make an infusion of 2 tablespoons of camomile heads to 1 pint (½ litre) of boiling water. Leave to cool, strain, and then repeatedly rinse the hair with it after washing and rinsing the hair through with clear water. Use this after every shampoo and you will soon transform hair that has lost its highlights.

A stronger dye-type mixture can be made by taking 4 tablespoons of camomile flower-heads to about 7 fl oz of boiling water. Pour the boiling water onto the heads, leave to stand for half an hour, strain, and then mix to a smooth paste with kaolin powder (kaolin powder can be obtained from a good chemist's shop). Apply the paste to the roots of the hair, and then gradually comb it through to the ends. Cover the hair with an old towel wrung out in hot water, then a layer of tinfoil and a shower cap to retain the heat. The first time you apply the dye, leave it for about twenty minutes only before rinsing out. If your hair is very porous, you will find that the hair will have lightened more than if the hair is non-porous. Try the dye this way once as a test run. If it does not have sufficient effect, leave it longer next time.

Rhubarb This much-maligned plant can also be used to lighten fair hair. Take three to four sticks of fresh rhubarb, cut it into pieces and simmer in just over ½ pint (300 ml) of water for thirty minutes. Remove from the heat, leave it to stand for another twenty minutes, strain off the liquid and use it as a rinse, or make up into a paste with kaolin powder as in the previous recipe for camomile dye. Use it in the same way, rinsing out thoroughly.

For Dark Hair

Sage Even if your hair is beginning to turn grey, it will help to improve the colour. Take 2 tablespoons of sage to 1 pint (½ litre) of boiling water. Leave to cool, strain and rinse the hair repeatedly with the liquid. Used in the same way as the camomile rinse, sage will build up a gradually darkening effect. A paste dye can be made with 4 tablespoons of sage to 7 fl oz of boiling water. Pour the water onto the herb, leave to stand for half an hour, strain, then mix with kaolin powder to a smooth paste. Apply and use in the same way as the camomile paste.

Rosemary and Sage These can be used in the same way, mixed as a rinsing liquid or as a dye paste. *Sage and raspberry* leaves make a good mixture, too.

Henna This is a traditional oriental hair colourant which has gained in popularity in the West over the last few years. Like many of the vegetable hair colours, henna gives the hair extra body and lustre. In general it brings out reddish highlights in most types of hair. There are several different shades of hennas available, even 'blonde' hennas. Ask what effect they are likely to have on the colour of your hair when you buy them, particularly if your natural colour is very light.

Henna is made from the ground leaves of a species of privet native to eastern regions such as Egypt. It usually comes in powder form. Mix the powder to a smooth paste with hot water (you can add a little olive oil or an egg yolk when the mixture has cooled down), apply to the hair, cover with an old towel, foil and a shower cap to retain the heat. Leave for anything from half an hour to two hours before rinsing out thoroughly. Henna is especially helpful to fine, oily hair, as it improves the texture and strength.

For Auburn Hair

Henna is a good treatment for auburn hair, reviving lost tones.

If you want to tone down the redness, add sage. Mix the henna with tea to highten the redness. Use *marigold* petals as a rinse to keep hair bright.

For Grey Hair

Hollyhock If your hair is well on the way to being white or silver, make the most of it in its natural state. To get rid of slightly dingy, yellowish tones that tend to make silver and white hair look dull, hollyhock flowers give a subtle bluish highlight. Choose fresh flowers that have bluish-purple tones, or find a supply of dried flowers and make an infusion. Use as a rinse or make a paste as in the camomile recipe for blondes.

Children's Hair

All of the shampoo recipes are suitable for young children. The soapwort-based shampoo is pleasant for all the family to use. For young babies suffering from cradle-cap, add lots of strong marigold petal infusion to the rinsing water. Obtain a pure marigold ointment (see marigold balm recipe on p. 64) and rub it gently onto the affected scalp. Marigold has very soothing effects on such scalp conditions.

Shaving and Hair Removal

Men

Shaving can be of great benefit to a man's complexion, because the act of shaving is a treatment in itself, removing as it does dead skin cells. The facial movements involved are good exercise for the muscles. Women can imitate these movements to help tone their faces!

How to Shave For wet shaving use a pure soap with marigold, comfrey or marshmallow extract. A very thin layer of moisturizer applied before soaping with a brush helps stop the skin drying out excessively. After shaving, tone the skin with a lotion.

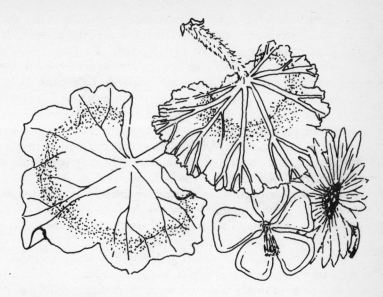

Rosemary and Sage Lotion
1 cup witch hazel
1 cup cider vinegar
½ oz (15 g) sage
½ oz (15 g) rosemary

Pour the cider vinegar into a screw-top jar. Add the sage and rosemary and leave to steep in the vinegar for a week. Strain the liquid off and add it to the witch hazel.

Pelargonium Lotion
1 oz (30 g) scented geranium leaves
1 cup cider vinegar

Scented-leaf geraniums come in a wonderful variety of fragrances, including lemon, wine, rose, nutmeg, peppermint and coconut. Infuse the leaves in the cider vinegar for ten to fourteen days, then strain off the liquid and use diluted after shaving. A fine-sprayer bottle is ideal for application, otherwise just pat it onto the skin.

A light moisturizer may be applied after shaving if the skin feels dry. If you have just shaved off a beard or moustache, the skin underneath may have become very slack and out of condition. Shaving itself will help to restore its firmness and tone. Use plenty of finger-tip massage, perhaps using marigold balm to improve any dry, flaky patches.

Beards and Moustaches The shape of a beard or moustache is a matter of personal taste, but most beards and moustaches benefit from grooming. Wash them every time you wash your face, using the finger tips to massage the skin underneath them. Dry, then apply a herbal oil such as oil of basil, rosemary or sage. Rub a little between the palms of the hands, then stroke a good-quality hairbrush over the hands to pick up the oil. Brush through the beard. A toothbrush can be a useful substitute when dealing with a moustache.

Women

Desirability of body hair on women is again affected by fashion and cultural background. However, heavy growths of facial hair can be an embarrassment. Fine, downy growth is attractive in many cases but whiskery or heavy growth may require treatment.

Facial Hair Women should never attempt to remove facial hair by shaving – you will end up with stubble and the need to shave almost as often as a man. If the hair is fairly fine, repeated application of lemon juice will help to bleach it gently. If this is ineffective and you do not like to use any of the commercial hair-removing preparations, electrolysis, carried out by a qualified operator, is the best answer. A number of sessions may be necessary, but it does offer a permanent solution. A small electric current is passed down into the hair follicle, killing off the root – a more or less painless process.

Underarm and Leg Hair In both cases shaving is probably the simplest and easiest method if you want to avoid commercial depilatory creams. You can use an electric razor or a hand-held wet razor. If your hair growth is fairly light and downy, you may regret shaving, because it will blunt the hair ends and make them appear coarser.

However, if you do decide to go ahead, using either method, make sure that you moisturize thoroughly after you have done the shaving. If you are wet shaving, apply a thin layer of moisturizer first, before working up a good lather with plenty of soap and water. Always make sure that you use a good sharp blade.

Waxing Hair removed by waxing regrows in a weakened state, so that eventually it becomes less necessary to remove it. This method is best used on long growths of hair.

You can make and use your own wax as follows.

Sugar Lemon Wax
1½ teaspoons glycerine
juice of two lemons
1 lb 2 oz (500 g) white sugar
strips of cotton fabric – old sheeting is ideal

Put the lemon juice into a saucepan, add the sugar and let it all melt slowly over a gentle heat. Cook gently for about eight to ten minutes until it turns a golden colour, then remove from the heat. Add the glycerine, mixing thoroughly, and use it as soon as it has cooled to a comfortable temperature, and before it gets too cold. Test for a comfortable temperature on the inside of the elbow.

Apply the wax in thin strips, going down the legs. A plastic spatula for spreading glue makes a good applicator, otherwise use an ordinary spatula. Press the wax against the legs, then apply a strip of cotton over the top of it, pressing it onto the wax. Draw the cloth towards you, against the hair growth, taking the hair and wax with it. When all the hair is removed, rinse the legs, pat dry gently and apply a moisturizer.

3. SKIN CARE

We tend to forget that our skin is alive. It acts as an organ of excretion and is a perfect window on how well our metabolisms are working. The skin on our face is particularly important, because most of our sense organs are situated on the head and our personalities are shown through our facial expression. Our skin is often the first thing other people notice about us and is usually one of our major health and beauty preoccupations.

The first thing to decide is what sort of skin you have, usually identified by certain conditions. The four types of skin dealt with in this chapter are: normal, dry, oily and combination. Sensitive skin and other problems associated with the skin are the subject of Chapter 5.

Normal Skin

Normal skin is soft and smooth, and has a slightly translucent quality or glow. It is reasonably elastic. If you press a clean tissue on your skin when you wake up in the morning and it comes away clean, you probably have normal skin. If, when you wash it with soap and water, there is no tightness afterwards, it is a normal skin.

Cleansers for Normal Skin
Soap and Water There have been many arguments over the suitability of soaps for washing the face. If you are happy with soap, make sure you use the best one you can find. This need

not be the most expensive. Some soaps are highly-coloured, highly-perfumed, richly-packaged, and can cause sensitive skins to react. Head for pure vegetable-oil soaps or make your own. A good soap should give a silky lather and will leave your skin soft and smooth.

The most effective regime for washing is to run a basin of warm water – not too cold or too hot – splash the water onto your face very thoroughly, then work up a lather of soap with your hands. Apply it to the face and neck, working from the breast-bone area up the throat, up and around the neck and behind the ears, making small rotating motions with the finger tips while moving them up and outwards on the face. Pay special attention around the chin and the nose, areas which get particularly dirty. Be very careful around the eye areas, and do not drag or pull at the skin.

Rinse the face very thoroughly with lots of fresh, warm water. Add a tablespoon of cider vinegar to the final rinse to correct the acid balance of the skin. You can gently blot off the excess moisture with a pad of clean cotton wool, or pat the skin very gently with a towel. Do not scrub or rub the skin with a towel – it is too abrasive for the face.

Soapwort Cleanser The root of soapwort provides one of the gentlest forms of soap for any skin.

1 oz (30 g) soapwort root
1¾ pints (1.05l) water

Chop or shred the root and boil it in water, letting it simmer in a covered saucepan for twenty-five minutes. Cool, then strain. It is easy to use if poured into a bottle with a pierced stopper from which it can be squirted.

Home-made Soap A good health food store can supply castile soap made from olive oil. It is usually available in large blocks. Use an ordinary grater to give the weight you require.

4 oz (100 g) camomile heads
10-12 oz (275-350 g) soap shavings

If you are using dried heads, put them in a saucepan and just cover with water. With fresh heads, pound them up before adding the water. Bring to the boil and simmer very gently for ten to fifteen minutes, keeping the mixture covered with a lid. Remove from the heat and leave to cool. Leave to infuse for eight hours. Strain the mixture and add to the soap shavings. Return to a saucepan and let the mixture melt together over a very low heat, stirring constantly. When all is thoroughly mixed, remove from the heat and allow to cool slightly. At this point you may add an essential oil to enhance the fragrance.

Now pour the mixture into moulds. These can be greased bun tins – the shell-pattern ones are attractive – small jelly moulds, or you can line or grease other containers. The less dense your soap bar is, the quicker it will dry. The time taken can be between a few hours and a few days, depending on the type of herb you use. When it is dry, unmould it, cut the soap up if necessary and wrap it in greaseproof or tissue paper. Other good herbs you can use instead of camomile are: marigold, meadowsweet, comfrey, marshmallow, elderflower.

Cleansing Lotions for Normal Skin
Cleansing lotions are useful if you do not like to use water on your skin. They are applied and removed with damp cotton wool. A toner must be used afterwards to remove any oily residue.

Basic Lotion
50 ml witch hazel
10 ml vegetable glycerine
40 ml herb infusion
a pinch of borax

For the herb infusion use any of the herbs mentioned in the previous soap recipe. Use about one tablespoon of herb, pour on 40 ml boiling water, leave to cool, then strain off the liquid. Dissolve the borax in the infusion and mix with the other ingredients. Keep in a capped bottle in a cool place, preferably in a refrigerator.

Yogurt Cleanser
Obtain a 'live' yogurt if possible
One 5 fl oz (150 g) carton natural yogurt
¼ pt (150 ml) herbal infusion

Once again choose any of the herbs described for the soap recipe. Pour ¼ pt (150 ml) boiling water on to two tablespoons of the herb, leave to cool, strain, then mix with the yogurt. Keep in a capped bottle or jar in the refrigerator.

Rose Lotion
1 oz (30 g) beeswax
3 fl oz (90 ml) almond oil
2 fl oz (60 ml) rose water
rose oil (optional)

Melt the beeswax in the top of a double boiler or a basin set in a pan of simmering water. Gradually add the almond oil drop by drop, beating constantly with a wooden spoon. Then gradually add the rose water, a little at a time. Remove the pan from the heat (or the basin from the saucepan) and continue stirring until the mixture is lukewarm. At this point you may add a few drops of essential oil of rose if you wish. Stir thoroughly, then pour the mixture into a suitable bottle. Put on the cap and keep shaking the mixture every few minutes until it has become entirely cold. Store in the fridge.

Cleansing Cream for Normal Skin
Cleansing creams are particularly good for more mature skins.
    Galen was a Greek physician working about AD 200. Below is a variation on his original recipe for a good cleansing cream.

Rose Cleansing Cream (from Galen's recipe)
    1½ tablespoons beeswax
    1 tablespoon emulsifying wax
    4 tablespoons almond oil
    6 tablespoons rose water
    ½ teaspoon borax
    essential oil of rose

Heat the rose water with the borax so that the borax dissolves. Meanwhile melt the waxes and oil together in a double boiler. When the waxes and oil are thoroughly melted and mixed, remove both containers from the heat and add the rose water slowly to the waxes and oil, stirring continuously until the mixture is cooler. Then add the rose oil. Continue stirring until completely cool, then put into a jar. This is a variation on the Rose Cleansing Lotion theme. It gives a thicker, creamier mixture. Keep it cool.

Toners for Normal Skin
Toners are a good idea after cleansing. They help to remove any remaining film of cleanser and improve the texture of the skin by closing open pores. They are applied on slightly dampened cotton wool. There are simple herb infusions which work well to tone the skin. Make an infusion using 2

tablespoons of dried herbs or flower heads to a pint of boiling
water (use three handfuls of fresh herbs or flowers). Leave the
mixture covered for an hour, strain and bottle. Good herbs
are: marigold, meadowsweet, comfrey, marshmallow, elderflower.

Plain rose water makes a good toner or, for a slightly more
astringent effect, combine:

75 ml rose water and
25 ml witch hazel

Occasional Cleansers and Masks for Normal Skin

Once or twice a week a scrub or a mask makes an extra-deep
cleansing and refining treatment. If your skin is sensitive do
not use the scrub, nor should you steam your face, but do
cleanse with your usual method very thoroughly. If your skin
is not oversensitive, proceed as follows: Before applying a
mask, your skin needs to be in a very clean, receptive state.
Cleanse and rinse your skin using a soap, lotion or cream,
rinse thoroughly, or wipe over the skin with a herbal infusion.
Leave the skin slightly damp. You may then apply the scrub
or mask. Prepare a bowl of hot water to lean over. Cover your
head with a towel and keep your face at least 1 ft (30 cm) from
the water. Stay in this position for about ten minutes, and
then apply the mask or scrub.

Simple Scrub
Mix:
1 handful dry oatmeal
1 handful ground almonds
1 handful bran

Keep this mixture in a screw-top jar. Moisten a handful of the
mixture with rose water and use to gently scrub at the skin.
Rinse thoroughly and tone.
Basic Face Mask The simplest masks are based on an egg or
two. To the egg(s) you can add any of the following: fine

oatmeal, ground almonds, almond oil, wheatgerm oil, olive oil, cider vinegar, honey, liquidized cucumber, mashed banana, mashed avocado, small amounts of herbal infusions. Experiment with different combinations and textures. Apply to the skin, leave for at least twenty minutes while you lie down and relax, preferably with your feet raised slightly above the level of your head. Do not use masks around the eyes. You may also isolate some of the ingredients from the egg and use them on their own. For example: ground almonds, cucumber, rose water, oatmeal, honey or wheatgerm oil.

Fruit and Vegetable Cream You can make this cleansing cream using peaches, water melon, cucumber or strawberries. In each case pulp and sieve the fruit.

3 teaspoons beeswax
4 teaspoons coconut oil
5 teaspoons olive oil
4 tablespoons fruit pulp
1 teaspoon glycerine
pinch borax

Melt the oils and beeswax together over a pan of boiling water. Meanwhile, heat the glycerine, borax and pulp until the borax has dissolved. Add the fruit mixture one drop at a time to the oils and wax mixture, stirring continuously. Keep mixing until the mixture is completely cool, then put into a jar and keep in the fridge. Use up as quickly as possible.

Moisturizers for Normal Skin

Moisturizers are best used on a slightly damp skin. Skin needs to hold in moisture to keep it looking plump, soft and smooth. When applied to a damp skin, moisturizers then hold the dampness within the skin surface cells.

Basic Cream Recipes (Both may be perfumed with a few drops of essential oil.)

Vegetable Oil Cream
3 teaspoons beeswax
3 teaspoons emulsifying wax
½ cup almond oil
¼ cup avocado or sesame or sunflower oil
3 tablespoons rose water

Put the waxes into a basin over a pan of water and add the vegetable oils. Heat the rose water separately, and add it drop by drop to the oil, stirring vigorously all the time. Remove it from the heat and stir occasionally until it is cool. This makes a fine cream which is nourishing to a normal skin.

Light Moisture Cream
2 tablespoons almond oil
2 tablespoons emulsifying wax
1 teaspoon lanolin
½ teaspoon borax
9 tablespoons orange or rose water
1½ teaspoons glycerine
1 teaspoon witch hazel

Melt the oils and waxes together in a basin over a pan of
water. In another bowl heat the borax, flower-water and
glycerine and add the witch hazel. Remove from the heat and
add the flower-water mixture drop by drop to the waxes and
oil, stirring constantly. Stir until cool. This produces a light
but nourishing cream suitable for normal skin.

Dry Skin

Dry skin often feels taut, particularly if washed with soap and
water. It usually has a fine, almost 'powdery' appearance;
very fine lines form easily around the eyes and mouth, and
there may be patches of flaky skin. The sebaceous glands are
not producing enough oils to keep moisture within the
complexion, and this leads to dehydration. External help is
needed and diet can be adapted to help the condition. The
condition known as eczema manifests itself as a serious dry
skin problem and is dealt with in the next chapter.

Cleansers for Dry Skin
Soap and Water You may find that soap and water is too drying
for your skin, leaving it taut and flaking. If so use lotions and
creams for cleansing. If you want to continue using water, you
can use the Soapwort Cleanser given on p. 39, or you can
make up the soap, using olive oil and Castile soap shavings,
following the Home-made Soap recipe on p. 39. Good herbs to
use to add to the flakes are: marigold, meadowsweet, comfrey,
marshmallow, elderflower, violets or pansies, lady's mantle
and houseleek. You can halve the herb infusion and add
honey to make up the other half of the volume.

Cleansing Lotion for Dry Skin
The three lotions for normal skin are gentle enough for a dry
skin, or you may like the extra richness of a cocoa butter
cleanser.

Cocoa Butter Cleanser
1 oz (30 g) lanolin
1 oz (30 g) cocoa butter
4 tablespoons sweet almond oil
4 tablespoons of strong camomile or violet infusion:
½ pint (300 ml) boiling water poured onto two tablespoons flowers

Put the cocoa butter, lanolin and almond oil into a bowl over a pan of simmering water. When they have melted together remove from the heat and add the flower infusion. Whisk up the mixture with a hand whisk or an electric mixer. When it is all well blended and cool, pour into a bottle or jar. Cover and keep cool.

Milk Cleanser
½ pt (300 ml) fresh milk
3 tablespoons of elderflower or meadowsweet or camomile

Let the flowers steep in the milk in a cool place for an hour. Then put milk and flowers into a saucepan and let the milk warm over a very, very gentle heat. Make sure that the milk does not boil, and take it from the heat before a skin forms on the surface. Let it cool and strain into a bottle. Cap and refrigerate.

For a cleansing cream, use the Fruit and Vegetable Cream recipe on p. 44. It is soothing for a dry skin because of the coconut and olive oils.

Toners for Dry Skin
Rose water makes an excellent, gentle toner for dry skin. An *elderflower* infusion of 2 tablespoons of flowers to 1 pint of boiling water left to cool is excellent.
Lime (linden blossom) flowers are made into an infusion in the same quantities as for elderflower toner. They help to smooth out wrinkles.

Flower-Water Toner
35 ml orange flower-water
35 ml rose water
35 ml water (warmed)
5 ml glycerine
a pinch of alum

Dissolve the alum in the warm water. When the water is cool add all the other ingredients. Pour into a bottle and shake vigorously. Shake before use.

Occasional Cleansers and Masks for Dry Skin

Dry skin will benefit from thorough cleansing, although it must be done gently. You can use the Simple Scrub (p. 48), combining a handful of fine oatmeal, ground almonds and bran, massaging the dampened mixture very gently with the finger tips upwards and outwards on the face. If using a mask, cleanse your skin thoroughly beforehand in the usual way, using water, cream or lotion, or by steaming gently over a herbal infusion as in the section for normal skin. Rinse the skin and leave it slightly damp before applying mask.

Basic Green Comfrey Pack
1 handful fresh comfrey leaves
4 tablespoons purified or boiled water

Pulp the comfrey leaves, either by using a pestle and mortar or an electric blender. Strain the pulp through a fine mesh, extracting as much juice as possible. Smooth the juice over the face and lie down for fifteen minutes. Rinse off with tepid water and pat the skin dry. Apply moisturizer. This is a soothing treatment for dry skin, especially if it is feeling parched and tight.

Honey and Mallow Pack
1 oz (30 g) cleaned, chopped marshmallow root

⅓ pt (200 ml) water
1 teaspoon honey
1 egg yolk

Soak the marshmallow root in cold water for twenty-four hours. Strain the liquid and mix 1 tablespoon with the other ingredients. Smooth over the skin and leave for fifteen to twenty minutes while lying down. Rinse off with tepid water, pat skin dry and apply moisturizer.

You may also use any of the combination of ingredients given for Basic Face Mask for normal skin (p. 43-4).

Moisturizers for Dry Skin
You may use the basic moisturizer creams given for normal skin, but you will benefit more from richer creams, which are very nourishing. Do not use too much at a time.

Carrot and Wheatgerm Oil Cream
6 tablespoons wheatgerm oil
6 tablespoons carrot oil (if you canot get carrot oil, use almond oil and pierce 6 capsules of vitamin A into it)
2 tablespoons lanolin
2 tablespoons beeswax
2 tablespoons emulsifying wax
12 tablespoons distilled water
1 teaspoon borax
4 drops tincture of benzoin

Melt the oils and waxes together in a basin over a pan of hot water. Dissolve the borax in the warmed, distilled water in a separate basin. Add the water carefully to the oils and waxes. Remove from the heat and keep beating until it is cooled a little. Add the tincture of benzoin and continue beating until it is cold. Pour into a clean jar and keep closed and cool. This has fairly good keeping qualities, but do not leave it in the heat or with the lid off.

Rich Cocoa Butter Cream
2 tablespoons almond oil
8 tablespoons sesame or sunflower oil
2 tablespoons beeswax
1 tablespoon honey
4 tablespoons emulsifying wax
4 tablespoons cocoa butter

Simply place all the ingredients in a basin over a pan of
simmering water, stirring constantly until they melt together.
Remove from the heat and stir occasionally until the cream
has cooled. Pour into a clean jar, cover and keep cool. This
cream smooths into the skin very easily. Do not use too much
at once.

Oily Skin

Oily skin results from overactive sebaceous glands. At best
this results in a muddy, sallow complexion, and the skin
appears coarse and shiny. Other problems are open pores,
blackheads and spots. (The condition of acne is dealt with in
the next chapter.) This skin type needs very thorough
cleansing and toning (but not with harsh astringents) to
improve the texture. A non-oily moisturizer is also a good
idea. One good thing about oily skin is that it is less prone to
showing signs of ageing than other types.

Cleansing is particularly important. An oily skin makes a
marvellous adhesive for dirt and grime, pores tend to be open
and become clogged, the skin cannot breathe and blackheads
and spots are caused by toxic build up on the pores. Eat
plenty of raw fruit and vegetables, and drink plenty of water
and herb teas.

Cleansers for Oily Skin
Soap and water It often seems to give a pleasant, fresh feeling to
oily skin if soap and water is used. Do take care not to use
harsh soaps as these can sometimes overdry the skin, which

excites the sebaceous glands into pouring out even more oil. Use the soapwort cleanser given for normal skin (p. 39) or, if you want to make your own soap, follow the home-made soap recipe (p. 39). To your soap shavings add an infusion of any of the following: rosemary, lavender, yarrow, horsetail, comfrey, lemon balm.

You may also add some oatmeal to the soap mixture to make more of a scrub bar. Another idea is to use a simple muslin bag filled with oatmeal and bran to cleanse an oily skin. Dip the filled bag or sachet in tepid water and rub gently over the face. Always use a final rinse with cider vinegar in the water, whichever method you use for cleansing.

Cleansing Milks for Oily Skins

Buttermilk and Yarrow Lotion
¼ pt (150 ml) boiling water
2 tablespoons yarrow
¼ pt (150 ml) buttermilk

Infuse the yarrow in the boiling water. Cool the mixture, strain off the liquid and add to the buttermilk. Pour into a clean bottle and keep in the refrigerator.

Yogurt Cleanser
¼ pt (150 ml) plain yogurt (live, if possible)
¼ pt (150 ml) herbal infusion (use rosemary, lavender, yarrow, horsetail, comfrey, raspberries or lemon balm – any of these separately, or one or two combined)

Generally speaking a lotion is a far better cleanser for an oily skin than a cream.

Toners for Oily Skin

Toners are absolutely vital for an oily skin. They help to keep greasiness at bay longer, refining the pores so that they cannot so easily become blocked. It is important, however, not to use very harsh astringents, especially those containing a lot of alcohol. With prolonged use they tend to make the skin become coarse and almost leathery in appearance.

Simple Infusions You can make up simple herbal infusions to act as toners. Use yarrow, rosemary, horsetail or sage. Make up a small quantity using 2 teaspoons of dried herb to 2 cups of water. Pour the boiling water onto the herb, stand until cool, then strain into a screw-top bottle and use as necessary.

> *Egg and Lemon Toner*
> 1 egg white
> equal volume of fresh lemon juice
> 2 tablespoons yarrow
> ¼ pt (150 ml) water

Make up the yarrow infusion by pouring the boiling water onto the herb and allowing it to stand until cool. Whisk the lemon juice and egg white together, then strain the infusion into them and pour into a screw-top bottle. Keep cool or refrigerate.

Sage Toning Lotion This recipe is best used for extremely oily skin. Sage is a fairly strong astringent herb and is especially effective for open pores. It has antiseptic properties, so if you get occasional outbreaks of spots it will be particularly helpful. Use perhaps twice a week, with the other lotions used between times.

> 2 tablespoons sage, chopped
> ¼ pt (150 ml) water
> ¼ pt (150 ml) cider vinegar
> pinch of alum (optional)

Make the sage infusion by pouring the boiling water onto the herb and leaving it to cool. Strain this liquid into the cider vinegar. If the skin is particularly lacking in tone, a pinch of alum dissolved in the cider vinegar will have an extra tightening effect. Keep it cool or refrigerate.

Masks and Scrubs for Oily Skin

To make a sallow, dull skin look bright, use the Simple Scrub given in the normal skin section (p. 43), especially last thing at night to remove the day's accumulated grime. In the morning use one of the cleansers given in this section. Always apply the masks to a cleaned, very slightly damp skin.

Simple Egg and Lemon Mask Separate an egg and put the yolk into a small cup or egg cup. Add two or three drops of lemon juice, mix together, and leave to stand for about half an hour. Then apply to the skin, leaving for about twenty minutes while you relax. Rinse off with tepid water, pat the skin almost dry and apply a moisturizer. You can use up the egg white in Egg and Lemon Toner.

Yogurt and Oatmeal Pack Quantities of fine oatmeal and plain yogurt (preferably live) can be combined together to form a smooth paste. This can be used alone with just a squeeze of fresh lemon juice added. Or you can combine it with any of the following: grated carrot, grated potato, pulped cucumber, mashed pear, mashed tomato, puréed parsley (purée parsley with a little water in a mortar and pestle or in a blender). All of these fruits and vegetables have good cleansing and refining properties. Leave for twenty minutes, then rinse with tepid water, pat dry and apply moisturizer.

Milk Pack
2 teaspoons dried milk powder
1 teaspoon honey
1 egg white
1 cup of horsetail or yarrow infusion, made with
2 tablespoons of herb.

Mix together the honey and dried milk. Make up the infusion of horsetail or yarrow and, when cool, strain it and add to the milk and honey. Whisk the egg white until fairly stiff and add it to the mixture. Spread over the skin and leave for twenty minutes. Rinse with tepid water, pat dry and apply moisturizer.

Peppermint Pack This is a stimulating and refreshing pack. *Do not* use it on a sensitive skin with a tendency to redness or broken veins.

   a handful of fresh peppermint leaves
   1 egg white
   kaolin powder
   ¼ of a cucumber

Put the peppermint leaves, egg white and cucumber into a blender and blend until a smooth purée is formed. If you do not have a blender, roughly chop the cucumber and put it through a sieve, chop the mint leaves and pound them in a pestle, then whisk the egg white and mix them all together. Add the vegetable mixture to enough kaolin powder to give a smooth paste, then apply to the face, leaving it for about fifteen minutes. Rinse off with tepid water, pat dry, apply moisturizer. The peppermint will probably give a slightly tingling sensation while it is on the skin.

Fuller's Earth Mask If your skin texture is dreadful, with open pores and a tendency to break out into spots at times, Fuller's Earth makes a good base for a mask. It contains minerals and helps to draw out impurities from the skin, refining open pores and helping to extract blackheads and cut down greasiness.

   1 egg white
   Fuller's Earth
   herb water (infusion of suitable 'greasy skin' herb)

Mix together the egg white, some Fuller's Earth and a small amount of herbal infusion to form a smooth paste. Amounts will vary, depending on the size of the egg white. Apply to the skin, leave for fifteen to twenty minutes, rinse with tepid water, pat skin dry. Apply moisturizer.

   In time you will feel confident to experiment by using any of the basic mask ingredients with various herbs and fruits and vegetables. Keep a record of your experiments.

Moisturizers for Oily Skin

Oily skin has plenty of oil to hold water in the skin structure, but this water content tends to diminish with age. It is particularly important to apply a moisturizer on the more delicate areas such as around the eyes, mouth and neck which may have a tendency to becoming lined.

Moisture Cream for Oily Skin If you want to use a moisturizer, particularly at night or if you are going out into rough weather, a cream may be the best answer. You can follow the Light Moisture Cream recipe given in the normal skin section (p. 45), as it is not over-rich or greasy. Keep cool or refrigerate.

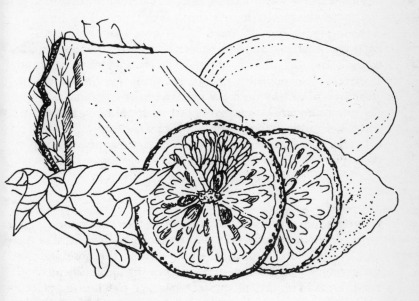

Lemon Cream Moisturizer
2 tablespoons fresh lemon juice strained
2 tablespoons witch hazel
4 tablespoons coconut oil (Coconut oil solidifies at room temperature, so warm the container in hot water to melt the oil.)

Put all these ingredients into a bowl and whisk them together very thoroughly, or put them into a blender goblet and blend until thoroughly mixed. Pour into a clean screw-top jar. Keep refrigerated or cool.

Raspberry Leaf Lotion
1 oz (30 g) beeswax
3 fl oz (90 ml) peach-kernel oil
2 teaspoons wheatgerm oil
1 tablespoon raspberry leaf infusion (infuse ½ oz (15 g) raspberry leaves in 1 cup of boiling water for 30 minutes, cool and strain)
1 tablespoon witch hazel
2 drops tincture of myrrh

Melt the beeswax and oils in a basin over a pan of boiling water, stirring with a spoon. Add the witch hazel and raspberry leaf infusion gradually, drop by drop, stirring constantly. Remove from the heat. Keep stirring and add the tincture of myrrh as it cools. When cool, pour it into a clean, screw-top bottle and continue shaking it occasionally until it is entirely cold. A little of this lotion goes a long way. Keep it cool.

Combination Skin

Combination skin is probably one of the commonest skin types. It is characterized by an oily panel in the centre of the face, so that the forehead, the area around the nose and the chin are prone to be shiny with a tendency to blackheads and open pores. The rest of the face has dry patches, especially around the eyes, possibly at the sides of the mouth, the cheeks and the neck. The best way to care for this skin is to regard it as two entirely separate complexions and to look after them individually. This means that in cleansing, toning and moisturizing you will select different methods for different localized areas.

Cleansing

Choose whatever method seems most comfortable; this might be soap and water or a lotion.

Toning

A slightly more astringent toner will be effective for the oily panel. Select one from the oily skin list. For the rest of the face choose a gentle toner from the normal or dry section.

Masks

Apply an oily skin mask only to the oily panel, where there may be open pores and blackheads. The rest of the skin may be treated with a milder mask. Choose from the normal or dry list.

Moisturizers

Apply a very light moisture lotion to the centre panel – this skin still needs moisture. To the rest of the skin you may apply an oilier, more nourishing cream or lotion. Select from the normal or dry list.

4. Skin Problems

Sensitive Skin

Sensitivity can be a problem in skins of varying degrees of dryness and oiliness. A sensitive skin will produce a smarting, tingling or burning sensation if certain substances are applied to it; it will have a high colour and broken veins. Suitable cleansers, toners, moisturizers, etc. can be used to improve the condition.

A sensitive skin reacts noticeably to a number of stimuli. When choosing products for your skin, avoid anything highly perfumed and any astringent lotion containing alcohol. Sensitive skin often displays signs of distress by blotchiness, redness, flushing and a tendency to broken veins. Keep a strict record of what ingredients you use for your cosmetics, so that you can avoid any substances which cause problems.

Diet

Keep a balanced diet, avoiding processed or 'convenience' foods. Many skin disturbances can be traced to reactions to certain preservatives, artificial flavourings and colourings. A yellow food dye, tartrazine, can give rise to a number of symptoms, not only skin disturbance, but also headaches and depression in some people. It is present in a surprisingly wide range of foods, including biscuits, cakes, pastries, sauces, preserves and pickles.

Limit your drinking of ordinary tea and coffee. Drink herb tea, particularly coltsfoot tea, which is probably one of the very best herbal remedies for thread veins.

Cut down on very spicy foods. Most spices or other foods and condiments which leave a hot taste in the mouth and make the face feel hot, including mustard and horseradish, should be excluded wherever possible.

Cut down or exclude alcohol, which drives fragile blood vessels to the surface of the skin.

Protect your skin with a suitable moisturizer if you are likely to be exposed to rough weather, whether cold, windy or hot. In hot sun, wear a sunscreen, plenty of moisturizer, and try to shade your face with an eyeshade or wear a wide-brimmed hat.

Take as much vitamin C as possible. Vitamin C cannot be stored by the body so you need a daily dose. It helps to maintain small veins and capillaries and prevents them from weakening and breaking down. Good sources of vitamin C are citrus fruits, green and red peppers, blackcurrants, rosehips, cauliflower, cabbage, strawberries, and potatoes (the vitamin C content of potatoes is concentrated under the skins, so avoid peeling.) Vitamin C tablets are available and can be taken as a supplement.

Vitamin E also helps to keep the structure of the skin in peak condition. It is present in wheatgerm, sunflower seeds, soya beans, ground nuts and corn, and any of the oils extracted from these plants.

Vitamin A is essential, too. Eat plenty of carrots, watercress and parsley. The importance of a mixed and balanced diet is vital for a sensitive skin.

Avoid extremes of temperature, particularly during the winter when it is common to go from heat indoors to very cold and biting weather outside. Always protect the skin with a moisturizer.

Acne

Acne is usually a temporary condition caused by an upset to the hormones, resulting in an overproduction of sebum by the sebaceous glands. The skin attracts grime and dirt to its greasy surface, pores become blocked and infections take hold, causing blackheads and inflamed spots.

Cleansers

Cleansing is of prime importance, but nothing too harsh should be used. Use the soapwort cleanser given for normal skin (p. 39), or a home-made soap. Use the Home-made Soap recipe (p. 39) given for normal skin with comfrey or yarrow as the herbal content. You might also add a small amount of sulphur powder, which has disinfectant properties and is a tried and tested substance to help with bad skin.

Herbal steaming can be particularly beneficial in treating acne. If you have a bad attack, you can gently steam the complexion every evening, using comfrey, sage or yarrow in the water. Keep the face at least 12 in (30 cm) from the water and cover the head with a towel. After three or four minutes the pores should be open and ready to receive a mask. Blot excess moisture from the face and then apply:

Comfrey and Kaolin Mask
6 fresh comfrey leaves, or infusion made by pouring 1 cup of
    boiling water onto 1 tablespoon dried comfrey
kaolin powder

Either sieve and pulp the fresh leaves to extract the juice, or strain off the cooled comfrey infusion and mix with enough kaolin powder to form a smooth paste. Leave for twenty minutes. Rinse off with tepid water and tone the skin gently with a comfrey or yarrow infusion, or use:

Sulphur Mask
1 egg white
1 teaspoon sulphur powder
2 tablespoons Fuller's Earth
small amount of healing herb infusion (comfrey or sage)

Mix these ingredients in suitable proportions to give a smooth paste. You will need more of the herbal infusion if the egg white is small, less if it is big. Apply in usual way. Rinse off after twenty minutes and then tone as in previous recipe, or use:

Sage Pack
1 tablespoon plain yogurt (preferably live)
2 tablespoons fine oatmeal
infusion of sage (2 tablespoons of herb to 1 cup boiling water – stand, cool and strain)

Mix together the oatmeal and yogurt, then add enough sage infusion to make a paste that will smooth easily over the skin. Leave for twenty minutes while you relax, then rinse off with tepid water. Pat skin dry gently, and then tone with comfrey infusion.

Internal Cleansers
Cleanliness of the internal system is absolutely vital with acne. Avoid too much starchy food, especially white flour products, very fatty foods or sugary foods. Keep chocolates and cakes to a minimum. Eat as much fresh fruit as possible and as many salads as possible. Drink as many glasses of fresh water every day as you can.

Start first thing in the morning with the juice of a lemon squeezed into a glass of hot water. It is very refreshing and gets the body systems on the go. Substitute herbal teas for ordinary ones. Many herbal teas are available in bags so that you can take them to work with you quite conveniently. Maté tea is an excellent tonic for the kidneys, which are the organs responsible for flushing toxins from the body. Rosehip tea is marvellous, too, because it is a good source of vitamin C. A course of yeast tablets will also be very helpful.

Do not fiddle with spots and blackheads – rely on the regular use of herbal steaming and applications of masks to bring them to the skin surface and expel them. When you begin an intensive course of steaming and masks, the skin condition often appears to get worse before it gets better. This is because many of the impurities lie well below the skin surface and the only way out is up through the skin. Drinking plenty of water and herbal teas will help to eliminate these impurities and toxins more rapidly.

Moisturizers for Acne

A lotion will probably feel better for daytime use than a cream. One can be made as follows:

4 tablespoons lanolin
2 tablespoons emulsifying wax
6 tablespoons beeswax
6 tablespoons avocado oil
strong comfrey infusion (2 tablespoons herb to 1 cup boiling
    water, cooled and strained)

First, take the oils and waxes and melt them together in a basin over a pan of simmering water. Mix them well together. Remove from the heat, cool, and then pour into a clean screw-top jar. Keep cool.

Make up the comfrey infusion and keep it for only a day or two in the refrigerator. To make the lotion, take two tablespoons of the oil and wax mixture, melt it and add a tablespoon of the comfrey infusion. Cool, then apply to the skin.

To make a comfrey cream, especially for use at night, take a good handful of fresh comfrey leaves and put them in a liquidizer. Strain the liquid off thoroughly and add it to the oils and waxes in the recipe above, while they are melting. The comfrey leaf-pulp can be kept and mixed with other ingredients as a face mask, or you can put it on your compost heap. If no fresh comfrey is available, use 2 tablespoons dried comfrey infused in a small cup of boiling water. Strain, and add a couple of tablespoons of liquid to the oils and waxes.

The basic oil and wax recipe above may be used with other herbs. A pinch of sulphur powder can be included to help clear the spots.

Acne usually clears up, given time and attention to what we put into our bodies, and what the environment is throwing at them. In very rare cases there can be difficult metabolic problems. Doctors are usually quite careful about prescribing antibiotics for skin conditions, but in some cases they will do so if all other treatments seem ineffective. If you do not see a conventional doctor, a homoeopathic doctor or a herbal practitioner may be able to help.

Eczema

Eczema is the name given to a number of similar skin conditions, usually characterized by excessive dryness and tightness of the skin. Sometimes it leads to the skin cracking, bleeding or weeping, normally accompanied by itchiness. The causes of eczema are numerous. Sometimes it seems to be an inherited tendency. It can be linked with asthma and hay fever, and be aggravated by tension or excessive tiredness, certain temperature or weather conditions; it may be a reaction to certain foodstuffs, such as additives, colourings, preservatives or natural foods such as cow's milk.

There are other forms caused by contact with particular substances, including strong soaps, especially those with high perfume and colour content, washing-up liquids and washing powders, nickel (in the form of money, cheaper costume jewellery or the studs on denim jeans!), wool, cats and dogs, certain mineral oils, flour, powder paints, cement, etc.

Diet and stress play a great part in the condition. Try substituting goat's milk for cow's milk. Avoid refined, processed foods. Take plenty of wholemeal flour products, nuts, yeast, B vitamins, sunflower oil, fresh fruit and vegetables. Try to find a way of relaxing to relieve tension – perhaps yoga or meditation, or going for a walk or a bike ride.

Cleansers for Eczema

It is possible to obtain 'emulsifying ointment' to use when washing the face or body. If this is unavailable, make up the basic Soapwort Cleanser given on p. 39 – this can be used for face or body.

Oatmeal Bag Make a small bag out of a piece of muslin and fill it with finely-ground oatmeal. Tie the top tightly. Then use the bag, having immersed it in water, to wash over the face, body and limbs.

At the same time hang another bag from your tap into the bath water. Fill it with any combination of the following herbs: camomile, comfrey, marigold, houseleek (having cut a leaf lengthways to reveal as much of its gelatinous inside as possible), birch bark, watercress, marshmallow, lime flowers (linden blossom).

You may find that cutting down the number of baths and showers that you take will help to alleviate some of the problems with eczema. Oils in the bathwater may help to prevent the skin from tightening up too much: try sunflower oil, almond oil, turkey red oil, any of which make excellent natural oils. Use about one or two teaspoons at a time. Turkey red oil is particularly good because it disperses in water and will not just float on the surface or leave a ring round the bath.

Toners and masks do not have a great part to play in treating eczema-affected skin, as it is usually very taut and dry as a result of the condition. Simple herb infusions can be used after cleansing.

Moisturizers or Soothing Preparations for Eczema

Marigold Balm
6 tablespoons almond oil
a good handful of marigold petals
4 tablespoons lanolin
2 tablespoons emulsifying wax
6 tablespoons beeswax

Put the marigolds into the bottom of a clean glass jar and pour on the almond oil, slightly warmed. Mash with a wooden spoon and then put on the lid. Leave the jar in a warm, sunny place for ten to fourteen days, shaking gently every day. At the end of that time strain the oil, first through a fine sieve and then through coffee filter-paper. Melt this oil with the lanolin and the waxes in a basin over a pan of hot water. Stir until all are thoroughly melted and blended. Remove from the heat, cool, put into a clean jar, and cap tightly. This balm is also excellent for a number of other conditions, including cradle-cap in babies, cold sores and chilblains.

Houseleek/Aloe Vera These plants both have fleshy leaves which, if cut lengthways, expose a gelatinous flesh. This is very soothing if placed directly on the eczema-affected area.

Yogurt and Carrot Soother Take a small 5 fl oz (150 g) pot of plain yogurt – live if possible. Grate a carrot finely and add it to the yogurt, stirring well. Put the mixture into the fridge or a cool larder and leave it to stand for several hours. Apply this to the

affected areas. If you do not have much time, dab on the plain yogurt on its own. It should relieve the itching very quickly.

It is possible to buy creams containing coal tar, camphor and sulphur which often prove very helpful in eczema and other bad skin conditons. Treating these conditions with attention to diet, relaxation and soothing and healing substances applied to the skin is far better than relying on the use of cortisone creams which have to be used with the utmost care because they can thin the skin and cause other problems. They tend to give some brief relief from symptoms but do not eradicate the underlying causes.

Shampoo Some people suffer from eczema on the scalp, or it is present around the hairline, ears, neck, or is irritated on the hands by contact with conventional shampoos. The best alternative is to make a strong infusion of soapwort which will cleanse without irritating. You can make a concentrated soapwort base and add small amounts of comfrey or camomile infusion.

Seborrhoeic Dermatitis

This is a form of eczema, the causes of which are not so easily identified or eradicated. It seems to give rather contradictory symptoms, in that the sebaceous glands are not working correctly – too much sebum is being produced, but the skin becomes flaky, red and rather dry. It occurs on the scalp, producing thick crusts of skin cells, thicker than dandruff flakes. The scalp may be sore and red and the hair-root becomes weak. As a scalp disorder this can lead to hair roots weakening and follicles 'giving up', resulting in areas where hair no longer grows. This is sometimes responsible for receding hairline in men. The hairline area may also be affected.

On the face it is usually limited to the areas around the eyebrows, nose and chin. On men the area where a beard grows is vulnerable. Patches of itchy, flaky skin may occur, and sometimes the patches may be weepy and crusts will form. Keep to a good diet and avoid using any harsh substances on the skin – follow instructions for basic eczema treatment. Stress often seems to play a part in this condition. If you are a woman make sure that you use make-up based on plant products. Mineral oils, chemicals and dyes can be especially irritating.

Psoriasis

This is a very distressing skin condition. It can be an inherited tendency or is sometimes brought on by emotional stress or shock. The skin can take on an almost reptilian apearance with scales of cells bunched together, because skin cells are being made at many times their normal rate. The skin looks almost silvery, and flakes are shed at an alarming rate. There is none of the smoothness and suppleness that one sees in normal skin.

Great claims have been made for going to the Dead Sea resorts in Israel to control and clear psoriasis. It seems that the extraordinary salinity and the 'mineral cocktail' of the sea water combined with the sun and relaxing atmosphere can do wonders for the most stubborn cases.

Sea and sunbathing are at the heart of the treatment. If you can afford it, give it a try, but for most of us home treatments can give very good results. Follow similar dietary advice as for eczema, paying particular attention to avoiding colourings, flavourings and preservatives.

Cleansers for Psoriasis

Use a very gentle cleanser such as the basic soapwort cleanser (p. 39), or use a coal tar soap. For shampooing the hair make up the soapwort infusion and combine it with herbs such as comfrey, birch bark, white willow or camomile. These same herbs may also be added to bath water by putting them into a muslin bag suspended from the tap.

Soothing Balm
1 oz (30 g) white willow bark
1 oz (30 g) comfrey root
1 oz (30 g) echinacea or 1 oz houseleek
1 oz (30 g) orange peel
1 pint (600 ml) water
anhydrous lanolin

Take the willow bark, comfrey root, echinacea or houseleek
and the orange peel, and place them in a saucepan with the
pint of water. Bring to the boil and then simmer for at least
twenty minutes. Remove from the heat, cool and strain
thoroughly. Save the herb solids for a muslin bath bag to be
used immediately if you like – or put them on the compost
heap. Take three parts of the herbal liquid and add one part of
melted anhydrous lanolin. Beat together until cold and put
into a clean glass jar. Use the balm to soothe the skin. If the
balm is rather thick and hard put some on a warmed spoon to
soften.

Use the balm regularly, especially if you notice an
improvement. The condition may clear up of its own accord
quite suddenly, but you must persevere with the treatment
over a long period. You should find that the balm spreads a
long way.

Also helpful is a drink, to be taken three times a day, made
by simmering ½ oz (15 g) inner bark of elm with 1 pint (600
ml) water. It is something of an acquired taste – you can
sweeten it with honey or hold your breath!

Cellulite

Cellulite is a word that promotes violent reactions from some
quarters. Some people claim that it is a condition invented by
fashionable doctors in order to make money out of worried
women. This may be so in some cases, but the fact remains
that some women do suffer from a skin condition where fatty
deposits, excess fluids and toxins become trapped under the

skin, making hard pads which look pitted like orange skin. The skin and fat structure of women is quite different from men, so men never get this problem.

The use of massage, herbal baths, herbal teas and regulation of diet combined with the right sort of exercise can do a lot to alleviate the condition. However, it demands perseverance and new attitudes to diet and exercise so that they become a way of life. If you are flabby and overweight you should do as much as you can to remedy the condition. However, there are many women without an ounce of spare fat who still suffer from pads of cellulite.

To a great extent the origins of cellulite lie in hormone production. When a girl reaches puberty, the hormones begin work and fat is laid down in certain areas, giving her the characteristic rounded feminine form, in the curvature of the breasts and, more particularly, in the pelvic region. It is in the pelvic region, between waist and knees, where cellulite occurs.

The connective tissue between fat and skin is such that the pockets of fat tend to be bunched up together. Oestrogen is the hormone responsible for triggering off the changes in the body at puberty, and an overproduction of oestrogen at this time, or during pregnancy, menopause or while taking the contraceptive pill, can lead to other side-effects such as fluid retention, with bloating, lethargy and lack of energy. The circulation is sluggish and lymphatic drainage is poor. The stagnant fluid and toxins lead to congestion and even slight inflamation in the connective tissues. The waste deposits are trapped, scar tissue of a fibrous nature develops and the trapped fat feels hard and grainy to the touch.

If you suffer from premenstrual tension or have any peculiarities of hormone function, check with your doctor. You may be lacking in progesterone and the doctor may be able to recommend some therapy. If you are under any emotional stresses and strains, this too can have a profound effect on hormone function. Also, if you spend most of the day standing, as a shop assistant or hairdresser for example, you may be prone to the condition. Even bad posture, skeletal

defects or back injury can put extra pressure on the pelvic
area.

Diet
Eat wholesome food. Steer clear of processed foods containing
colouring, flavourings and preservatives. Cut down fat and
alcohol, wean yourself off salt, seasonings and spices, and
sugar. Eat plenty of fresh vegetables and fruit. If possible, eat
little and often. Include the following in your diet: fresh fish,
lean meat (chicken is ideal), eggs, natural yogurt (live, if
possible), skimmed milk, wheatgerm, honey, raw fruits –
including grapefruit, pineapple, grapes and prunes, raw
vegetables – particularly watercress, sorrel, asparagus,
radishes and onions.

Taking extra fluid will not make the fluid retention worse if
you drink the right things. Take maté tea (which stimulates
the kidneys), comfrey tea (improves circulation), or fennel tea
(helps with elimination). Drink as much water as possible –
about eight glasses a day. If you live in a hard water area, the
tap water should be suitable, but if you do not like it or live in
a soft water area, take non-carbonated mineral water.

Exercise
The quality of the exercise is all-important. Avoid any activity
which puts strain on the leg muscles or jars the hips and
thighs. Do not go in for running, jogging, full ballet dancing,
riding, squash, tennis or strenuous aerobic type workouts.
Aim for something involving gentle, rhythmic movements of a
sinuous nature, activities which should leave you feeling
mentally calm. Ideal are fairly brisk walking, cycling,
swimming and yoga. These will help to improve circulation
and muscle tone without strain. If you do suffer from stress or
tension, they will also help your mental state, which in turn
affects your body.

Bathing and Massage
Massage is probably one of the greatest weapons in fighting

the condition, and it is quite easy to do this for yourself. The ideal time is after a bath, before which you may have taken some exercise or done some yoga. The bath will help prepare your skin for the massage. If possible take a sauna or go into a steam-cabinet. These treatments both help the skin to excrete toxins and waste matters through perspiration. Otherwise, have a leisurely bath whenever possible to relax you and calm the nerves.

Bath Water Additives In a muslin bag put any of the following: marjoram (oregano), horsetail, fennel seeds, broom flowers, seaweed – preferably bladderwrack, ivy leaves. Tie the bag and hang it into the water. You can also tip some Epsom Salts into the bath water. Fill a muslin bag with sea salt, have a soak in the Epsom Salts water, then stand up and rub the salt bag over the body. Make upward, rotating motions on the cellulite areas. Get back into the water and soak for twenty minutes. Then get out of the water and dry yourself, again making rotating motions on the cellulite areas.

Massage Oils and Potions for Cellulite

3 fl oz (90 ml) coconut oil
1 fl oz (30 ml) lemon oil
¼ fl oz (8 ml) lime oil or grapefruit oil

or

3 fl oz (90 ml) coconut oil
1 fl oz (30 ml) lemongrass oil

Mix the oils together and use them to massage into the troublesome areas. The coconut oil is the massage medium and the lemon, lime, grapefruit or lemongrass oils are the active ingredients which help to get the circulation of fluids back to good condition.

Seaweed Pods If you live near a beach you should gather seaweed, particularly bladderwrack. Pop the blisters on the bladderwrack leaves and squeeze out the gel-like substance inside them. Use this goo to massage the cellulite areas. If the goo is too thick to rub in easily, mix it with a little vodka, which will help to carry the seaweed gel into the skin. (Vodka is used because it is the nearest thing to neat alcohol. To use neat alcohol you must have a special licence!)

Broom Oil Gather broom flowers while they are out, or you may be able to obtain them dried from a specialist source. If you can sustain enough constant warmth to keep coconut oil in a liquid state, bruise the broom flowers and let them macerate in a jar of the oil for several days. Otherwise, bruise the flowers and let them macerate in almond oil for several days. Leave the jar on a sunny window-sill. When the time is up, filter to strain out the pieces of flower, and use this oil for massage.

Massage Movements

To massage effectively, to carry the active ingredients through the congested tissue, a number of particular movements are helpful. If you find some of the more pressing, forceful movements uncomfortable, try carrying them out while in the bath – underwater they feel less severe. Then concentrate on the other movements when you have applied your massage oil.

Stroking Movements This is done to apply the oil. Relax the hands and then stroke them over the areas on which you are working, making an upward movement towards the heart. Start very gently, to soothe and relax, and then become more firm to get the circulation going.

Rolling Movements Take up an inch or so of flesh between your thumbs, making a pressing and rolling movement. Concentrate this on areas where the cellulite is especially bad.

Kneading Movements Take the flesh with your hands, as if you were kneading a piece of dough, pressing it and squeezing it as you go. This is another good movement to make on particularly fatty areas.

Knuckling Movements Use the knuckles as a marvellous tool for applying pressure and stimulating the flesh.

Wringing Movements Take up the fatty flesh almost as if it were a cloth to be wrung out, squeezing and twisting as you go.

Rotary Movements Use the thumbs and finger tips to apply rotary movements to small areas of skin, particularly as a finishing movement after some of the more strenuous massage techniques.

Slapping Vigorous slapping with the hands flat, with cupped hands or the edges of the hands is marvellous for stimulating circulation and bringing a glow to the skin. However, be careful if you have a tendency to broken veins – many people are prone to them, particularly at the tops of the thighs. Avoid slapping in such areas.

Wrinkles

Everybody develops wrinkles eventually, some earlier than others, depending on skin type and certain other conditions. We should not regard them as an absolute disaster – they can add charm to a face when they are laughter lines around the eyes. Anyway, it is more honest to accept them gracefully than to resort to plastic surgery.

How To Avoid Them

Make sure that you pay extra attention to applying moisturizer to the areas around the eyes and at the sides of the mouth. Dab the moisturizer on very gently with the finger tips – never drag or pull at the delicate skin around the eyes. The same applies to removing make-up. Use a very gentle oil to 'float' make-up off rather than something heavy to wipe it away.

Try to keep a relaxed expression if at all possible. It is difficult to concentrate on not frowning, but with practice it becomes easier. Do not lie sunbathing with you face exposed to the sun. It is very ageing to the delicate facial skin, and you are also likely to squint, wrinkling up the skin around your eyes. If you have to be in bright light, get a good pair of sunglasses that cut out glare.

Smoking can make the problem worse. For one thing you

may well squint as you draw on the cigarette, and for another you use up vast amounts of vitamin C which helps to keep the structure of the skin healthy.

Apricot, Almond and Wheatgerm Oil
1 fl oz (30 ml) apricot oil
1 fl oz (30 ml) almond oil
1 fl oz (30 ml) wheatgerm oil

Put these oils together into a screw-top bottle and shake thoroughly. Dab a little on the skin around the eyes, mouth and neck – anywhere that lines are forming. This is best done last thing at night. The oils will soon sink into the skin and help to plump out lines.

Again, make sure that you eat a good diet with sufficient protein and vitamins, perhaps taking a course of yeast tablets too.

Freckles

Freckles look very attractive on most people. However, if you have them and wish to play them down, you can gradually erase them by applying yogurt or buttermilk with horseradish grated into it. Apply the mixture, leave for fifteen minutes, then rinse off and pat the skin dry.

5. SKIN PLUS...

The history of make-up and colour cosmetics goes back to ancient times. Early attempts at visual expression are more likely to have been ritual body-painting and tatooing rather than painting or drawing on any other surface. In our civilization the main idea of make-up is to enhance the face, by camouflaging certain less attractive features, such as a very red nose, and drawing attention to more attractive parts of the face such as the mouth and eyes.

Like most skills, accomplished use of make-up comes with practice, the use of the right tools and materials and, even more importantly, a good surface on which to work. The skin must be as clean and smooth as possible. If you follow the ideas in the skin-care section you will be on your way to achieving as near-perfect a complexion as possible.

Equipment

There are certain items of basic equipment you will need. It pays to buy the best tools you can afford and to take care of them. Always have plenty of clean cotton wool and soft tissues available, plus cleansers, and gentle eye make-up remover. Brushes and applicators give the most professional-looking finish and the following twelve items makes a comprehensive kit:

1. A narrow, pointed brush for gently tracing fine lines of liquid or cake-liner along the upper eyelashes.

2. A fairly flat, squared-off brush for applying feathers of dark powder shadow along the crease of the upper eyelid.
3. A chiselled, narrow brush to apply powder eye-shadow over most of the eyelid.
4. A fine, flat brush for outlining the lips.
5. A very fine, pointed brush for upper-eyelid liner, and for applying powder just below lower-lid lashes.
6. A sponge applicator for blending dry powder shadow or dampened powder eye shadow.
7. A brush for block mascara, to make the lashes look feathery.
8. A small, soft brush for gently dusting on traces of highlighter over browbone and eyelids.
9. A medium-sized, oval-ended brush for flicking away any excess shadow, and for general tidying-up purposes.
10. A very large fan-shaped brush for dusting off surplus powder from the face and for re-applying loose powder to small areas.
11. A smaller brush for applying highlighter around the eye sockets and cheekbone areas.
12. A large, chubby brush for applying blusher to the cheeks.

There are some excellent synthetic alternatives to sable brushes available now. Keep your brushes clean, particularly those used for cream products. Wash them out gently in a soapwort solution to remove greasiness, then wipe them dry on a clean piece of tissue, making sure that they keep their shape. Let them dry naturally in the air.

Applying Make-up

Prepare your skin by thorough cleansing, toning and then moisturizing. Let the moisturizer sink in well for ten minutes or so. This will leave the skin in the best condition for accepting the make-up base, usually referred to as a foundation. One of the major purposes of applying a foundation is to even out the tone of the skin, making it a prepared 'canvas' on which the art of make-up can be worked. Shop around carefully for a colour suitable for your natural skin tone and always try it out on your face. Do not choose a shade lighter or darker than your natural skin tone. Unless you have an exceptionally florid complexion, a combination of foundation and a standard concealer should be sufficient. However, if your colouring is very 'high', you may need one of the green-tinted foundations to counteract this tendency. A 'concealer', usually in stick form, will hide most blemishes, as well as eradicating shadows between the bridge of the nose and the eyes.

To apply a foundation, use a small cosmetic sponge, wetting it and squeezing out the moisture so that it is just damp. Dot the foundation on the face with a clean finger tip, then use the damp sponge to blend the make-up into the skin, working out to the hairline, taking it gently over the eyelids and just under the chin

Powder is not always necessary, but it does help to 'set' the make-up. Experiment to find what suits you. Choose a transparent powder and use a velor puff or a piece of cotton wool to press it gently onto the skin. Never rub it on to the face – it will merely dislodge the foundation, and rubbing is not good for the conditon of your skin. Remove any excess with a soft brush.

Blusher helps to emphasize the cheek-bones. It comes in two forms, powder and cream. The cream versions should always be used before powdering, blending them with a sponge or the finger tips. Powder blushers should always be used after powdering with the transparent powder. To place the blusher correctly, work outwards from the point below the centre of your eye, leaving a good inch clear of your hairline.

Eye make-up leaves plenty of room for experimenting. You can use make-up with great subtlety, purely to enhance what is already there, or you can go overboard for the most dramatic effects. Eye colour and definition is available in several forms – powders, creams and pencils. Use good quality pencils which glide colour over the delicate skin as easily as possible. A stiff, hard pencil tip will often soften if it is gently warmed in the hands before use.

Kohl pencils are very soft and particularly good for the under-eye area. Use brushes to subtly blend one colour into the next. Unless you have very long, thick lashes which are dark to the very ends, you will probably find mascara necessary to add the final touch. Find a mascara that is not so soft that it smudges and comes off in blobs, but also avoid the very hard-to-remove kinds. Apply downwards on top lashes and upwards on the bottom lashes.

For the lips, it helps to carry foundation over them in the initial stages of make-up. Apply colour by using a lip pencil to outline the lips. You can adjust your natural lip line fractionally if you feel it necessary, then fill in with a conventional lipstick, putting the colour on with a brush and finishing with a gloss.

Eyebrow Care

At present there is a tendency to leave eyebrows as natural-looking as possible. However, even the most natural-looking eyebrows will need some care and attention, probably including occasional plucking to tidy them. Keep plucking to a minimum. The aim is to have a neat brow and to give a good balance to the face and features.

Most straggly hairs occur beneath the brow in the area where highlighter or other colour is normally applied. These should be plucked away. Take care when plucking any odd hairs above the brow. Remove them only if they are obviously untidy.

The best time to carry out plucking is in the evening before going to bed. Any redness of the skin will die down as you sleep. A good time is immediately after a bath, which will have opened the pores. Or you can apply a clean hot flannel or pad of cotton wool to open them. With a wedge-shaped pair of tweezers, take each hair as close to the root as possible, and pull quickly and firmly. Once all the stragglers have been removed, dab the area with a piece of cotton wool wrung out in astringent or a comfrey infusion.

A small brush can be used to keep the eyebrows smooth, to remove dust and flakes of dead skin. Dry patches of skin will benefit from moisturizing.

Making Your Own Make-up

It is impossible to make a vast range of colour cosmetics at home – certainly nothing to compare with commercial products. However, it is possible to make a few colourful concoctions. It should be understood that the maximum 'shelf life' of home-made cosmetics is two or three days, and then only when they are kept in a fridge.

Lip Gloss
1 teaspoon alkanet root
2 fl oz (60 ml) almond oil
½ oz (15 g) beeswax

Crush the alkanet root and infuse it in the almond oil for ten days to a fortnight. Strain the oil and melt it with the beeswax, mixing well. Beat until cold. Use as a gloss for the lips.

Lipstick
2 tablespoons alkanet root
4 fl oz (120 ml) sesame seed oil
4 tablespoons cocoa butter or beeswax

Leave the alkanet root to infuse in the sesame oil for two weeks. Strain the oil, melt the cocoa butter or beeswax in a small basin, and then add the oil, beating them together. When cold pour it into a small screw-topped jar and use to colour the lips.

Eye Shadow
4 fl oz (120 ml) sesame oil
1 oz (30 g) colouring leaf or flower (various plants suggested below)
1 oz (30 g) beeswax

For a plummy-coloured eyeshadow take black or blue malva flowers (malva is the mallow family of flowers). Heat the flowers very gently in the oil until the colour is released. Add the beeswax and as soon as it has melted, remove from the heat and beat until cold. Keep it in a small, screw-top pot.

For a green colour substitute parsley. You can add chlorophyll colouring separately as the beeswax is added to give a more intense colour. A small piece of chopped beetroot yields good colour. Blackberries or blackcurrants may also be used.

Tanning and Exposure to the Sun

We all need a certain amount of sunlight for a healthy supply of vitamin D, and psychologically sun is good for our well-being. However, there is considerable evidence that indiscriminate exposure to sun, especially on the delicate facial skin, results in premature ageing of the skin, making it thick and coarse. In some countries, such as Australia, prolonged exposure to strong sunlight can lead to skin cancers in those with fair skins. In temperate regions such risks are very small indeed, but care should be taken to prevent the discomfort of burning.

Whenever you tan you must always be liberal with moisture. Put on plenty of moisturizer, particularly around the mouth and eyes. Wear a wide-brimmed hat and/or good quality sun-glasses to prevent squinting and screwing up the eyes. The tan is formed by the skin producing a substance called melanin, a protective pigment. The sun's rays stimulate the production of pigment. Northern European skin types have very little melanin compared with those of tropical and equatorial regions. Fair-skinned people should build up a tan gradually. Take care if you have thread veins, as sun exposure can make them worse. Take extra vitamins C and B because sunbathing seems to use them up quickly.

Tanning Lotions
Although the following natural lotions are helpful, they do not protect the skin against sunburn as well as good commercial products.

Mayonnaise Make up a basic one-egg mayonnaise, then add an extra tablespoon of fresh lemon juice and use this mixture as your lotion.

Tropical Lotion
2 fl oz (60 ml) coconut oil
1 oz (30 g) cocoa butter
1 fl oz (30 ml) sesame oil
Few drops of perfume oil (an exotic flower-oil is good)

Combine all the oils together, perfuming if desired. This lotion is good for an easy-to-tan skin, but not for the fairest skins.

Tea and Sesame Lotion
1 cup of strong tea (use four teabags, put them in a pot and pour on one cup boiling water)
¾ cup sesame oil

Make the tea, leave it to infuse until cool, then add it to the sesame oil, shaking them up together. Shake the bottle every time you use it. Sesame oil is good for absorbing ultraviolet rays, and the tannin content of the tea acts as a natural sunscreen, so it can be used on a more sensitive skin than the previous recipe.

Comfrey Tanning Cream
1 oz (30 g) comfrey root, soaked in one cup of cold water for twenty-four hours.
2 tablespoons wheatgerm oil
3 fl oz (90 ml) sesame oil
1 oz (30 g) lanolin

Melt the oils and lanolin together in a basin over a pan of simmering water. Heat 3 tablespoons of the water in which the comfrey root has been soaking, and when the oils have melted, add the comfrey water to them, drop by drop, stirring vigorously all the time. Remove from the heat and continue stirring until cold. Transfer to a screw-top jar. The comfrey is soothing and healing and the wheatgerm oil has marvellous properties for keeping skin healthy.

Treating Sunburn
Despite taking precautions it is still possible to become sunburned. If you are severely burned or feel very ill, go to a doctor immediately. For most cases, the following treatments will help:
Yogurt Plain yogurt smeared over the affected areas is cooling and soothing.

Comfrey Lotion Take a good handful of fresh leaves or a heaped tablespoon of dried leaves, put in a pan with one cup of water, bring to the boil and simmer for twenty minutes. Cool and strain, then apply to the burnt skin.

Cold Tea Strained, cold tea, a fairly strong brew if possible, takes away stinging and irritation very quickly.

Milk Works in a similar way to yogurt.

Cucumber Slices of cucumber are instantly cooling.

Potato Poultice Grate raw potato and spread on the skin. It may be easier to use it grated fine and wrapped in a piece of muslin.

Aloe Vera/Houseleek Gel Take a leaf from either of these plants, slit it lengthways and use the gelatinous juice to soothe the skin.

When your tan is beginning to flake or fade and the skin is looking sluggish, use scrubs, containing oats or bran, to loosen dead skin cells. To make the skin whiter, use combinations of buttermilk, yogurt, strawberries and lemon. For your face you can mix any of these, together with Fuller's Earth, as a pack. For the body, apply them as lotions and leave for as long as possible before rinsing. Moisturize afterwards. You can preserve the glow of a tan longer by making sure that you keep moisturizing the skin as much as possible. This will delay the fading and flaking considerably.

6. THE BODY

You could use all the ideas in this book and do yourself a certain amount of good. But real success depends on your attitude to your whole being, both physical and mental.

A basis for a healthy body is undoubtedly diet and exercise. Much advice on both is available, and it is sufficient here to summarize current ideas.

Diet

Eat a balanced diet, cutting back on fats, sugars and salt. Take plenty of fibrous foods. Substitute beans, pulses and nuts for some meat dishes. Eat as much raw fruit and vegetables as you can. Use plenty of herbs in all your dishes. If you miss taking as much salt as you used to, the herby flavours will do more than compensate.

There are numerous good cookery books dealing with the use of herbs in everyday cooking. There is not enough room to deal here with what you can try, suffice to say that there are such subtleties of flavour, either when herbs are used alone or in combination with each other, that they will open up a completely different way of seasoning and flavouring dishes.

Mint is usually associated with lamb – it also marries beautifully with yogurt or with cucumber or tomato or even raspberries! Sage and onion is usually associated with pork, but sage can be used in many meat mixtures and pork can be given a beautiful flavour with tarragon. The conventional seasoning of salt and pepper can be replaced or augmented hundreds of times over.

If you drink alcohol, do so in moderation. Do not drink alone!

Drink as much water as you can. If tap water does not appeal to you, try some of the bottled mineral waters. Many of them contain traces of minerals which act as a tonic to the system. Drinking a glass of hot water with the juice of a lemon squeezed into it is a good wake-up drink. Dring four or five glasses of water throughout the day if you can.

Herbal Tea

Experiment with herbal teas. They are a pleasure to drink in themselves, aiding relaxation, conditioning all of the body, improving hair and complexion, and helping to relieve stress, tension and sleeplessness.

Herbal teas are one of the pleasantest ways of enjoying the benefits of herbs. They are normally made by taking a teaspoon of herb per person, putting it into a china teapot (not a metal one), pouring on boiling water and leaving it to stand for four minutes, before straining the tea into a cup. Drink it unsweetened, or with a little honey or a slice of lemon. If you wish to make a tea using seeds instead of herb leaves, add bruised seeds to a pan of boiling water and simmer for five minutes before straining.

Camomile Tea This is good if you are feeling 'off colour' or have an upset stomach.

Raspberry Leaf Tea A marvellous tea to drink regularly during the latter months of pregnancy and up to confinement, as it helps to relax the uterus and makes the birth less painful. Can also be used to relieve period pains.

Lime Flower (Linden Blossom) Tea Do not let it stand too long before drinking. It has a delicate flavour and helps to relieve stress and make sleep more calm.

Peppermint Tea This is good if you have a cold. Peppermint also works very well if you have indigestion or flatulence.

Spearmint Tea A good, refreshing tea – drink anytime.

Valerian Tea This is made from the root of the valerian plant and is about the best herb for insomnia (hops are also good).

However, do not use it day after day over a long period of time. Leave it for a while after a fortnight's use.

Comfrey Tea This is a herb that is useful for any number of problems: coughs, stomach ulcers, mouth ulcers or just as an occasional tonic.

Lemon Balm Tea A pleasant, delicately flavoured tea. Delicious iced as a summer drink.

Sage Tea The Chinese wondered why the West wanted to buy oriental tea when they already had sage of their own! This is a good tea to drink, particularly if you have a cold or a sore throat. Sage tea has disinfectant qualities and also helps as a general internal tonic.

Toning Up with Massage

An excellent supplement to a programme of healthy exercise is massage. It is of tremendous value for relaxation, circulation, muscle tone and a general sense of well being. You can achieve a lot on your own, and slightly more if you have someone else with you.

Face, Shoulders and Neck

A great deal of tension can be stored in these areas, resulting in headaches and a general feeling of agitation. Facial massage can be carried out with a light moisture lotion, making light, upward and outward strokes, but avoiding the delicate skin around the eyes. (A recipe for this lotion is given on p. 45.)

Concentrate on stroking movements to the forehead and temples. Firm finger-tip pressure to the temples will sometimes help with tension headaches, as it will on the hard bone behind the bottom of the ear and at the back of the neck.

Use your left hand to massage your right shoulder and vice versa. Make stroking and kneading movements. Then use firm rotary movements with the finger tips to release tension around the shoulder blade, working inwards towards the spine. Then work upwards towards the neck and hairline, and then gently around to the front of the neck.

Lower and Middle Back
Rotary movements of varying pressure along the spine area are very relaxing. Then move the hands outwards, using the thumbs to press out the tension. Finish with pinching and pressing movements in the flesh above the hips.

Arms
Start at the wrist and work upwards. Press and push around the wrists and elbows. Knead and pinch the flesh thoroughly on the upper arm, particularly the backs of the arms, where pockets of fat can develop.

Chest or Breasts
Make large rotary finger tip movements, upwards and outwards, taking care not to drag at the skin.

Stomach
Use large, circular movements with the hand flat. Then, using both hands, take any spare flesh on the lower abdomen or over the hips and knead it thoroughly, finishing off with small, rotary finger-tip strokes. Pinch up any flab on the upper abdomen (diaphragm) area.

Bottom
You can afford to include the hip area again while you are massaging the bottom. Start with deep, open-handed stroking. Then proceed to knead, knuckle, wring and pinch, finishing off with small rotary movements with the finger tips.

Thighs
Begin with upward stroking. Knead, knuckle, wring and pinch again, finishing with rapid, short upward strokes. Concentrate pinching and wringing on the backs and inside of the thighs.

Knees
Another area where fat can sit all too comfortably. Pinch and

press all around the knee area, finishing with firm small rotary movements.

Calves
Make long, firm upward stroking movements, and gently knead away any areas of muscular tension.

Ankles and Feet
Stroke the whole foot, top, bottom and sides, finishing with the thumb and forefinger stroking up around the heel. Make small rotary movements and press gently all around the toes, then along the soles, sides and insteps. Take your time over feet. You can do a foot massage alone to counteract stress built up during the day. Time is needed because the muscle and structure of the foot is about the most complex part of the whole anatomy.

Hands
Manipulate the joints and press gently, keeping all the motion in the direction from fingertips to wrists. Fuller treatments for hands are given in the next section.

Care of the Hands

Hands are the human being's primary tool. As such, they take a great deal of punishment, mainly from external sources. Whether you are a man or a woman your main aim should be to have hands which reflect your helath, with flexible skin and strong clean nails. Few of us can have the lily-white hands expected of Scarlett O'Hara, but at least we can aim to protect them from harsh treatment.

General Care
Whenever possible, avoid direct contact with harsh detergents and cleansers, including washing-up liquid, scouring powders, cleansers and washing powder. Gardening, working on car engines or other machinery all take their toll. Wear gloves

whenever you can, or a barrier cream, and use plenty of nourishing hand cream every time you wash and dry hands.

Old-Fashioned Hand Lotion
1 fl oz (30 ml) glycerine
4 fl oz (120 ml) rose water

Put these ingredients together in a jar and shake well.

Soothing Marshmallow Cream
1 oz (30 g) scraped and finely chopped marshmallow root
¼ pt (120 ml) cold water
1 tablespoon beeswax
1 tablespoon cocoa butter
1 tablespoon sweet almond oil
1 teaspoon lemon juice

Soak the marshmallow root in the cold water for twenty-four hours, gently pressing the root occasionally with a wooden spoon. Strain the liquid off and set to one side. Gently melt the beeswax, cocoa butter and almond oil together over a low heat. Stir in the lemon juice and one tablespoon of the marshmallow root decoction. Stir together well, remove from the heat and stir until it is cold. Then pour into a screw-top jar.

Camomile Lotion
2 teaspoons carragheen moss
4 tablespoons surgical spirit
2 tablespoons camomile infusion (1 tablespoon herb to 4 fl oz (120 ml) boiling water, cooled and strained)

Melt the carragheen moss in a little hot water. Add to the spirit, glycerine and the two tablespoons of camomile infusion. Mix together well, adding a few drops of camomile essential oil if desired. Then pour into a screw-top jar.

Marigold Barrier Cream
1 tablespoon strong marigold infusion (1 tablespoon to 4 fl oz (120 ml) boiling water, cooled and strained)
2 tablespoons almond oil
2 teaspoons kaolin powder

Mix all ingredients together. Work the cream well into the hands before any dirty or hand-wearing jobs. When finished, wash the hands with a gentle soap. Dry thoroughly and apply a hand cream or lotion.

Watch out for eczema on the hands. Read the section on eczema on p. 63 and be particularly careful about what you expose your hands to daily – something like handling money can trigger eczema.

Removing Stains from Hands The skin on the hands can become stained very easily – sometimes by quite simple things like peeling potatoes and onion skins. The juice of the potatoes is an effective stain-remover. Lemon juice is a favourite old remedy, or you can rub the stains with the inner skins of any citrus fruit. The juice of sorrel leaves is also very effective.

Hand Packs These packs are a little messy but well worth the effort. They can also be used on rough skin on the feet.

> 2 heaped tablespoons ground almonds or fine oatmeal
> 1 tablespoon honey
> 1 egg yolk, beaten to a froth
> cotton gloves and large light-weight plastic gloves (cotton socks and plastic bags if applying to the feet)

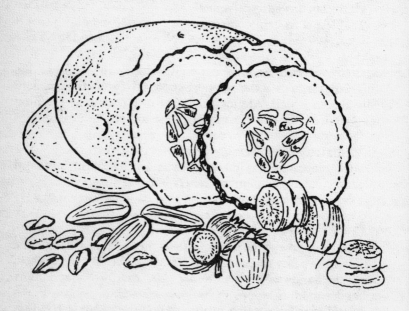

Mix the ingredients together to a smooth paste. Apply the paste, concentrating on the areas which are particularly rough. You will find it helpful to have another person to put the gloves on your hands. If possible keep the gloves on overnight. They may leak onto the bed clothes, so a large pair of plastic gloves or even plastic bags worn over the top will avoid this hazard. At least keep the gloves on through the evening. Rinse the hands afterwards and apply a cream or lotion. With repeated application, this hand pack will help the roughest and most neglected hands.

Rose Water and Almond Paste Mix ground almonds and rose water with a little milk to a paste. You may also add a little olive oil or orris root powder, varying the proportions so that you get a smooth paste.

Sugar and Oil Rub/Salt and Oil Rub A little coarse sea salt and olive oil, or sugar and olive oil, rubbed into grimy, rough, stained hands helps to remove the stains and soften the skin.

Nails

Nails are made of keratin, the same substance as hair. The nail we see is 'dead', and the growing area of nail is below the cuticle. Poor health is often reflected in the state of the nails: brittleness, cracking, splitting and lack of lustre.

Attention to diet may be necessary. Eat plenty of protein in the form of lean meat, fish, beans, nuts, pulses, eggs, cheese, fresh fruit and raw or lightly-cooked vegetables. The B vitamins, contained in bread, yeast, oatmeal, etc. – are important. A supplement of B vitamins or brewer's yeast tablets can be useful. Some people find eating a cube of jelly every day helpful. If you do not want to take any of the colouring or flavourings of table jellies, seaweed capsules could be the answer, particularly those containing kelp.

Nail Massage
Massaging the nails helps to improve circulation, stimulates growth and strengthens them. You may simply massage in oil with your fingertips, or better still, buff the nails with a special nail buffer or a piece of cloth. A nail buffer is usually a soft pad covered in fine leather. A piece of velvet or soft, closely woven natural cloth wrapped around a ball of cotton wool is just as effective. Massage with almond oil or use a little block of beeswax, working either substance into the nail very well, and then polishing to a sheen.

Hangnails

This is a condition when little pieces of cuticle break away, so that a tiny strip of skin peels down at the side of the fingernail. Try not to pick at these pieces of skin. They should be left alone or they will become inflamed and sore. Make sure that you are taking in enough protein and vitamin C.

Cuticles

Whenever you wash your hands, gently push the cuticles back with a towel. Always use plenty of cream or lotion around the cuticles. You can massage them using 1 teaspoon kaolin powder and 1 teaspoon lanolin.

Use emery boards to shape the nails, not metal files. Avoid cutting the fingernails with scissors. Clean out under the nails with an orange stick (a round-ended wooden stick). Try to file only in one direction. Massage nails and apply handcream after manicure.

Stained Nails

Nails can become stained, particularly if you smoke. Simply paint lemon juice onto them twice a day, using a small paintbrush.

If they are very badly stained, mix together:

1 teaspoon glycerine
5 teaspoons rose water
4 teaspoons hydrogen peroxide (5 vol.)

Removing Nail Varnish

If you wear varnish, give your nails a rest from it occasionally. Whenever you remove varnish, make sure to use an oily remover containing glycerine, which helps prevent the acetone drying out the nails too much.

Warts

Never attempt to cut warts – you will just make matters

worse. There are a number of infusions which will help to get rid of warts: these include ivy and bluebell flowers.

Make up a strong infusion as follows: 2 tablespoons of herb to ¼ pt (150 ml) boiling water, cooled and strained. Apply to a small piece of lint and bandage over the wart. Change once or twice a day until the wart softens and comes away.

An extra effective method is to use the juice of greater celandine. The juice is squeezed from the stem. Take care to apply it only to the wart. Wash it off immediately if it touches other parts of the skin – it will peel away healthy skin if allowed to remain. Do not cover it with a bandage. Apply twice a day. Within a fortnight the wart should have flaked away, leaving healthy skin.

Age Spots on the Hands

These large, freckle-like spots on the backs of the hands, sometimes spreading up the arms, are usually part of the natural ageing process. Lack of B complex vitamins, vitamins E and C can also make the problem worse. Increase your intake of them and rub in wheatgerm oil. You can use fresh lemon juice for its bleaching effect, or use yogurt with horseradish grated in.

Feet

Many of the treatments for hands can be applied equally well to the feet. Most of us take our feet very much for granted, until we get very tired or develop a painful corn. The foot is a wonderfully complex piece of machinery on which we depend for the whole of our balance and ease of movement.

When you can, go barefoot, and let the foot relax in its natural state.

Wise choice of footwear is important. Aim for shoes which do not pinch or squeeze the foot, with heels of a comfortable height. Unfortunately, fashion often dictates differently. But try to avoid tight, pointed toes and high, flimsy heels. These are responsible for ruining a lot of healthy feet by distorting bones, rubbing blisters and corns and putting strain on the calves, upper legs and pelvis. Such shoes can throw the spine and the whole body into an unnatural and uncomfortable position.

Socks and Tights

Tights are almost always man-made, and very few of us can afford the luxury of silk stockings. Stockings are healthier for many women, because they leave the crotch area relatively unconfined, cutting down the likelihood of problems such as thrush. Choose tights that fit comfortably and wash them out in soap flakes or soapwort mixture. The same applies to socks. If possible choose socks made of pure wool (or a mainly wool mixture), or cotton ones for summer.

Pedicure

Use massage, moisturizers and foot packs to keep your feet supple and smooth. Cut toe nails straight across to avoid ingrowing nails, which can become very painful. Use a pumice stone to rub away areas of very hard or rough skin. Do this every time you wash your feet, and be generous with moisturizing afterwards. You can use one of the hand moisturizers for this. If you have bunions (swollen toe joints) or bad corns or callouses, see a chiropodist.

Smelly Feet

Men seem to suffer with this complaint more than women. Wear natural fibre socks or stockings. Change your socks or stockings every day, and try not to wear the same pair of shoes day after day. Synthetic material shoes can cause the problem, but the biggest offenders are often plimsolls and canvas summery shoes. An old-fashioned remedy is to use potassium permanganate crystals dissolved in water as a foot-wash.

Wash your feet with soapwort mixture or your own herbal soap. Dry thoroughly, paying attention to the area between the toes. Then dust the feet lightly with a powder, such as the following:

Foot Powder
pure, unscented talc, or
powdered orris root added to:
powdered orange or lemon peel,
or fine powdered sandalwood

Mix these and use every day.

Also useful is a foot rinse or soak, made as a strong decoction of sage or lovage, both of which have good deodorizing properties. Take a couple of tablespoons of the herbs and simmer them for about half an hour in ½ pint (300 ml) of water. Strain and cool. Wash the feet or soak them in the liquid.

Try to eat sage, lovage and parsley fresh in your diet, as well as live yogurt. These foods seem to have the effect of reducing all unpleasant body odours.

Cold Feet

This is primarily a circulation problem. Take plenty of exercise and drink comfrey tea, which helps to improve circulation. Also make sure that you have enough vitamin E in your diet, as it plays an important part in circulation. Massage is very helpful.

Wear shoes and boots that are not too tight – a small pocket of air all around the foot keeps it warm. There are very effective inner soles for shoes, which seem to keep the cold out. They have a silvery surface and are available in most department stores. Leg-warmers rolled down around the ankles are helpful.

Athlete's Foot

Athlete's foot is characterized by soft, peeling skin between the toes. The feet will feel unusually clammy and are likely to be smelly. This is a fungal infection which thrives where the acid balance of the skin on the foot has tilted too far to the alkaline. The condition is infectious, so do not walk about barefoot where other people are likely to tread.

Bathe the feet with soapwort mixture, and dry very thoroughly with a towel or piece of cloth, which must be kept for your use only. Boil after use. If you are just washing your feet, do so with soapwort, and then add cider vinegar to your rinsing water. Use arrowroot powder to dust between the toes when they are well dried.

Treatment Foot Bath
1 oz (30 g) agrimony
1 oz (30 g) onion (finely chopped)
1 oz (30 g) sage
1 oz (30 g) red clover (optional)
1 oz (30 g) broken walnut shells (optional)
5 pts (3 litres) water
2 tablespoons cider vinegar

Simmer all the herbs in the water for twenty minutes. Strain them out and put the herb solids to one side. Cool the liquid and add the cider vinegar. Pour into a basin and immerse your feet immediately, soaking them for fifteen to twenty minutes. Then pack the strained herb solids between your toes. Leave them there for another twenty to thirty minutes. Finaly, rinse your feet, using water with added cider vinegar, and then dry thoroughly. Wear thin, natural fibre socks.

Verrucae

A verruca, also known as a plantar wart, is a wart growing into the foot. Usually a little group of black dots or a single black dot is at the centre of it. The condition is infectious so do not go barefoot and keep your towels and footwear away from other people's. Follow the treatment given for warts on the hand.

Most effective is the greater celandine stem juice. Buy a packet of round corn pads, stick one round the verruca, paint the juice onto the verruca and cover it with a fresh strip of plaster. Apply the juice twice a day, and soon the verruca will just peel away. In exceptionally stubborn cases, it may be necessary to go to the doctor for treatment.

Comforting Foot Baths

Fill a large bowl with warm water. Add a tablespoon of washing soda crystals and add handfuls of rosemary, comfrey, camomile, lavender, yarrow, mint, pine needles, sage or geranium leaves – any or all of them. It is less messy to pack the herbs loosely in a thin muslin bag, tied and immersed in the water. A pinch or two of alum powder is desirable for its toning properties.

Sea salt is comforting to tired, sore feed. A pinch or two of mustard powder is invigorating, especially if you have come in with cold, wet feet.

Chilblains

This conditon is the result of poor circulation and exposure to sudden changes in temperature. Chilblains can occur on the hands, or more usually on the toes, characterized by an area of tender and inflamed skin, and tissue which feels stinging and uncomfortable. Keep warm, keep moving, and take comfrey tea for circulation.

Make up marigold balm as given on p. 64 in the eczema section. Rub gently onto the chilblains and it should soon bring relief. For broken chilblains, make a strong infusion of marigold flowers and comfrey leaves. Strain the herbs out, putting them to one side. Cool the infusion to blood heat, and soak the chilblains. Then put the marigold and comfrey pulp onto them, leaving as long as possible.

Horseradish and Yogurt Grate a little fresh horseradish root and apply to the chilblains whenever possible.

Mouth and Teeth

A few minutes spent each day on this part of your body pays dividends. Many people do not realize the value of their teeth until they are threatened with losing them. Modern dentistry is aimed very much at preventative measures, but there is a lot you can do to help yourself.

Cleaning Your Teeth

Choose a brush with rounded bristles that is not too hard. Over zealous use of hard brushes can do more harm than good. Hold the brush at an angle of 40° to the teeth and, starting at the back, gradually work you way round with a slightly rotary movement to lift out any food lodged between the teeth. Clean all the teeth surfaces – you will soon notice by running your tongue over them whether they are clean or not. Make sure your brush also gently massages the gums. It is possible to lose perfectly good teeth by having unhealthy gums. If your gums are at all spongy, soft or red, or if they bleed when you clean your teeth, go to a dentist immediately.

Plaque is a hard build up that tends to sit between the teeth or around the edge of the gums. Thorough, regular brushing should keep it at bay, but use dental floss to get at awkward areas. Toothpicks are also useful.

Tooth Cleaners Herbal toothpastes are available, or you may wish to make your own cleansers.

Salt and Bicarb
3 tablespoons bicarbonate of soda
2 tablespoons fine sea salt

Simply mix these two ingredients together, and store in a jar. Shake a little into the hand and pick it up on the brush.

Burnt Toast
couple of slices of burnt toast
peppermint oil

Charcoal is a good cleanser! Crush the toast (in a blender, with a pestle and mortar, or crushed inside a polythene bag with a rolling pin). Add a few drops of peppermint oil and use the powder to clean the teeth. Rinse very thoroughly to remove any black bits left between the teeth.

Sage Leaves and Strawberries Fresh sage leaves and strawberries can both be used to rub over and around the teeth to clean and polish them, and to sweeten the breath.

Mouthwash Here is a pleasant mouthwash which helps keep the gums in a state of good repair. It needs time to stand during the making.

½ cup vodka
1 oz (30 g) powdered myrrh
peppermint or spearmint oil

Add the myrrh to the vodka in a screw-top bottle. Stand for ten to fourteen days, shaking daily. Strain through coffee filter-paper, and then add a couple of drops of mint oil. Dilute this with water and use it to rinse out the mouth.

Do not eat lots of sticky sweets and cakes, especially between meals. High fibre foods, wholewheat flour products, plenty of fresh vegetables and fruit, plenty of protein, calcium and vitamins are all vital. If you eat garlic, chew some fresh parsley or fresh mint leaves and you will avoid inflicting it on others. If you want the health benefits of garlic without the odour you can take deodorized 'garlic pearls'. Bad breath can result from food decaying around the teeth, from digestive problems or through catarrh or throat infections. If it is a persistent problem see a doctor.

Lips

Lips look and feel at their best when they are soft and smooth. Sun, wind and cold can all cause cracked lips, as can certain substances in lipsticks. Buy lipsticks made with vegetable ingredients and vegetable dyes. In the meantime you can make a pot of lip balm.

½ oz (15 g) beeswax
½ oz (15 g) cocoa butter
½ oz (15 g) lanolin
½ fl oz (15 ml) apricot oil
½ fl oz (15 ml) wheatgerm oil

Melt all the ingredients together in a basin over a pan of simmering water. Stir very thoroughly, remove from the heat, cool and add a flavouring if you wish – an oil, mint, orange, lemon – or even an essence such as vanilla (make sure it is pure vanilla and not vanillin). A few drops should be enough. Keep in a screw-top jar.

Mouth Ulcers

These crop up in most of us from time to time. If you have a number of them over a long period, there may be a problem with your metabolism. Whether they are present singly and occasionally or more often, a course of brewer's yeast tablets may help. To relieve the discomfort take:

1 heaped tablespoon dried comfrey (4 or 5 fresh leaves)
1 cup of boiling water

Pour the boiling water over the leaves and leave to stand for 10 minutes. Strain off the liquid and save the leaf pulp. Use the liquid as a mouthwash, holding it in the part of the mouth where the ulcer is for as long as possible before spitting it out. Use up the whole cupful of liquid in this way. Next, if you can spare the time not to talk, pack the leaf pulp into the mouth over the ulcer and leave it there for as long as you can, an hour if possible. Then rinse the mouth out to get rid of any odd bits of leaf. This has been known to heal large and uncomfortable ulcers very quickly.

Cold Sores
These uncomfortable little sores break out around the mouth. They are caused by a virus similar in nature to that which causes chicken pox and shingles, known as the 'herpes virus'. They usually occur when one is not in the best of health, perhaps with a cold or flu, or as the result of a bad diet or stress.

Obtain some tincture of camphor and dab on at the first sign of a sore developing. You may also find the marigold balm (given on p. 64) a soothing and helpful remedy.

Eyes

Eyes are delicate mechanisms and should be treated with the utmost respect. Any trouble should be taken immediately to a doctor or an ophthalmic optician. Sleep and relaxation help to keep eyes looking clear and bright, as does a good mixed diet. If you lack sleep or have been overindulging in alcohol, too rich foods or tobacco, then the appearance of your eyes will suffer. Make sure that you take plenty of vitamin A (found in carrots and apricots).

Eyewashes
If your eyes feel sore and tired, an eyewash may be very helpful. However, before making anything you should ensure that everything you use is scrupulously clean. Pads and

compresses should be sterile to begin with, then thrown away or re-sterilized. Any washes should be used up straightaway and not stored, not even in a refrigerator.

Use 'Eyebright' herb or 'Clary sage' to make your eyewash, using 1 tablespoon of herb to a cup of water. Make a decoction by boiling the herb in the water for twenty minutes, and then cooling it. Strain out several times, preferably through coffee filter-paper to remove any tiny pieces of herb. Then soak pads in the mixture, or use an eyebath. If your eyes feel sore all the time, do consult a doctor for advice.

Simple Eye Pads

If you are tired and your eyelids feel heavy, lie down in a quiet shady room, with your feet raised above the level of your head. Apply any of the following to the eyelids:

Tea-Bags Squeeze out the excess moisture and wait until they have cooled down before applying.

Thin Slices of Raw Potato Excellent for relieving any slight puffiness or a bruised sensation.

Slices of Cucumber Wonderfully cooling and soothing and also has properties to help keep wrinkles at bay.

If you wear a lot of eye make-up, use a very fine oil to remove it so that is floats off. Then use the apricot, almond and wheatgerm oil mixture (see p. 74), dabbing it gently with the finger tips around the eye area.

Bath Time

The basic function of a bath or shower is to clean the skin. But when you can make the time, use your bath as an opportunity for a general therapy session. Try some of these ideas given below.

Extremes of temperature are to be avoided. Water that is too hot or too cold can be a shock to the system, and leads to overstimulation of sebaceous glands or damage to delicate blood-vessels. Have the water comfortably warm, so that a splash with tepid water, either in the bath or shower, should be enough to close the pores.

Bath Additives

Oils Use vegetable oils if possible. Sunflower oil, coconut oil or almond oil are excellent, and use turkey red oil if you want one that disperses in the water. Keep the oils in bottles or jars in the bathroom, and add essential perfume oils to them. There is a whole range of exotic aromas to choose from: jasmine, rose, honeysuckle, lemon verbena, gardenia, sandalwood, camomile. These are just a few, but you can try any essential oils.

Salt A generous handful of sea salt is particularly beneficial if you have any broken or sore skin or scars to be healed.

Herbs The neatest way to include herbs in your bath water is to put them into a calico or muslin bag, tie up the top and suspend it in the water on a string. You can combine herbs or use them singly.

Invigorating Herbs Rosemary, borage, peppermint, nettles (do not use too many at a time), mustard, yarrow, pine needles.

Herbs to Soothe Sore Skin Comfrey, seaweed, marigold, woodruff, violets, lady's mantle, marshmallow, houseleek, aloe vera, camomile, elderflowers, birch bark.

For a Refreshing Bath Spearmint, lavender, lemon verbena, salad burnet.

For a Relaxing Bath Sage, lavender, rose petals, angelica, valeria, lime flowers (linden blossom), elderflowers.

Take some fine oatmeal or rice, cook until soft and transfer the solids and all the soothing liquids to a calico bag. Hang in the bath water.

Loofahs

A loofah is the dry, fibrous part of a vegetable gourd. It makes a marvellous piece of equipment for sloughing off dead skin cells and improving circulation. You can buy loofahs whole (they are usually sold flat – you soak them and they blow up into their familiar marrow shape), or you can buy loofah mitts with a towelling surface on one side and a loofah fibre surface on the other. Use the loofah on danger areas for spots or rough skin.

Oil and Salt

For areas of tired, dingy, rough skin, particularly during and
after winter when we tend to wrap up in layers of clothes, rub
with a spoonful of sunflower oil mixed with a spoonful of salt.
You can substitute sugar for the salt or use sea salt on its own.

Body Packs

You can use packs on problem areas of the body as you would
on the face. It helps to have someone else to apply the
mixtures for you, but you should be able to manage on your
own. If you have a spotty back, use Comfrey and Kaolin Mask
or Sulphur Mask or Sage Pack from the section on acne,
which begins on p. 59. Either wash your back thoroughly and
apply the mask, or if you have just taken a bath, let the water
run out, remain sitting in the bath, let your back air dry, then
apply the mask – your skin should be well cleansed and the
pores receptive. You can lie face down in the bath, but more
relaxing, lay face down on the bed for fifteen minutes. Then
rise the pack off with tepid water and pat yourself dry.

If you have dry, goose-pimply skin on your legs,
particularly on the top, outer thighs, make up a body pack
before you take a bath. You need: half a cucumber, fine
oatmeal, olive oil, rose water and honey.

Cut the cucumber into chunks then sieve it or put it into a
blender. Meanwhile, put about half a cup of rose water into a
saucepan, add fine oatmeal and cook gently for a few minutes.
You should add enough oatmeal to make quite a stiff mixture,
so that when you remove it from the heat and add the pulped
cucumber, the mixture will stick to the skin and not slide off.

Have your bath, let the water out, but lie where you are. Let
the air dry your skin until it is barely damp. Apply the
mixture and leave it on for twenty minutes. Then splash off
with tepid water and pat dry. Apply a body lotion afterwards.
You may need to do one section of the body per session –
unless you can stand up having applied it to the buttocks and
thighs.

Lotions and Massage Oils

After a bath or shower is the best time for applying body lotions or massage oils.

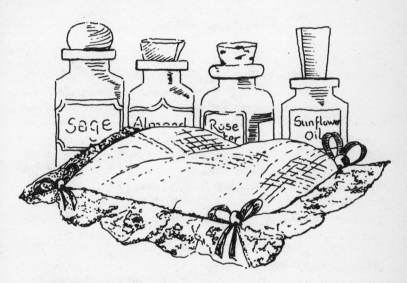

Honey Body Lotion
2 oz (60 g) anhydrous lanolin
1 fl oz (30 ml) sunflower oil
1 fl oz (30 ml) almond oil
1 fl oz (30 ml) wheatgerm oil
2 fl oz (60 ml) rose water
essential oil of your choice

Melt the lanolin in a basin over a pan of simmering water. When melted, add the honey, stirring constantly. Then add the oils and finally the rose water, drop by drop, still stirring all the time. Remove from the heat, cool down and when still barely warm add the essential oil if you want to use one. Pour into a clean, screw-top bottle and shake occasionally until thoroughly cold.

Rich Cocoa Butter Lotion
1 oz (30 g) anhydrous lanolin
1 oz (30 g) cocoa butter
3 fl oz (90 ml) sunflower oil, or 2 fl oz (60 ml) sunflower oil
    and 1 fl oz (30 ml) almond oil
2 fl oz (60 ml) orange flower-water
essential oil of your choice

Follow the instructions as for previous recipe, melting the
lanolin and cocoa butter, then adding the oils and finally the
flower water drop by drop, stirring all the time. A carnation
oil goes well with this combination of ingredients. The cocoa
butter makes it extra rich.

Use these lotions liberally all over the body. Remember that
the neck needs moisturizing and massaging as much as the
face. Be liberal with moisture creams or lotions around the
collarbone and neck, using firm, upward strokes. For the
breasts, make the lotion up as for Rich Cocoa Butter Lotion,
but substitute 2 fl oz (60 ml) strong infusion of lady's mantle
for the flower water.

Massage Oils
You can use sunflower oil or almond oil, peach kernel or
avocado oil for basic massage.

You may like to take a large bottle or jar and into it put half
a tablespoon to a tablespoon of any or all of these ingredients:
lavender, sage, orange peel, rosemary, lemon verbena, lemon
peel, marigold.

Pour on sunflower oil, screw on the lid and shake the
mixture. Leave the bottle on a warm, sunny window-sill for a
couple of weeks, shaking the mixture vigorously every day.
When the fortnight is up, pour the oil into a clean vessel
through a fine sieve, then carefully through filter paper. Keep
filtering until the oil is as clear as possible.

When applying body lotion or massage oil stroke it on with
the finger tips, applying it with strokes upwards on the arms
and legs, upwards and outwards on the trunk and across the

shoulders. Make small rotary movements on areas of muscular tension. Make small, pinching movements on small areas of fat – this helps to break down the fat globules.

Sleep Pillows and Sachets

People who have found other methods unsatisfactory have been greatly helped with sleeping problems by the use of herb pillows. A vast amount of herbs would be needed to fill a pillow. It is better to make a small cushion on which you can rest your neck or cheeks while you are in bed or relaxing in a chair. Or make a simple muslin sachet which you can slip underneath the pillow-case.

Use muslin, cotton or linen. Man-made fibres can cause a build-up of static electricity, making the skin feel clammy, and preventing the aromas passing through the material.

Suitable Herbs for Sleep Inducement
Hops (one of the most sedative herbs available), sweet woodruff, lady's bedstraw, bergamot, rose petals, mint, thyme, lavender, rosemary, lemon verbena, angelica, marjoram (oregano), sage, valerian (use very, very sparingly).

To make a small cushion or pillow, combine herbs as desired and put into a small muslin sachet. This can be sewn up or tied. Insert this muslin sachet into the middle of the stuffing you have chosen for the pillow – clean feathers or a natural-fibre wadding or filling. Cover with pretty cotton fabric, leaving one end sewn in big stitches so that the cover can be easily removed for washing and the herb sachet removed from the stuffing. The herbs will need replacing after prolonged use.

For an under-the-pillowslip sachet of about 6 × 8 in (15 cm × 20 cm), use muslin or another very loosely woven cotton fabric, filling it with suitable herbs.

For a soothing, clean fragrance, combine marjoram and lemon verbena with a little thyme and mint.

Lavender combined with a little lemon thyme, lemon

verbena and sweet woodruff is a good combination, particularly if one is feeling stuffy and headachy. Lavender is well known as a cure for headaches, particularly where they have been induced by tension. For a comforting fragrance, combine lady's bedstraw, hops, rose petals, a little marjoram and a little crushed vanilla pod.

7. HERBS AROUND THE HOUSE

If you turn to herbs in your diet and in the external care of your body, then you may feel inclined to have herbs about you in your living environment. Some research suggests that aerosols have harmful effects on the outer layers of the earth's atmosphere, and there is some doubt as to the effects that exposure to the aerosol propellants may have on us. It is possible to replace aerosol air-fresheners with herbal preparations.

Pot-Pourri

Pot-pourri is the name given to mixtures of petals and leaves of assorted plants, sometimes combined with other ingredients such as spices and oils. A mixture can be set in open bowls to scent rooms or placed in other containers, or used to fill bags or cushions. There are no really hard and fast rules for making pot-pourri. You may wish to experiment with your own variations on basic recipes. It is very important to write down what you have put into a blend, because you may come up with a really stunning fragrance; not having the combinations and proportions of ingredients to reproduce it would be most frustrating.

Always pick disease-free blooms and leaves, and avoid picking them after rain or while dew is still on them. Pick on a warm, dry day and dry them away from strong light in an airy, dry place.

When you are blending, put the flowers and leaves into a

large bowl, mixing them well. Then add a fixative such as orris root, gum benzoin, costmary or sandalwood. Fixatives help to stop the essential oils in the plants from evaporating. Next add spices, then other fragrancing substances such as chips of cedar or sandalwood, lemon, orange or other citrus peels dried and pounded to a powder, cinnamon sticks, vanilla pods or cloves. Finally, drop by drop, add fragrant oils. Be very careful when adding spices and oils, as too much can overpower the subtleties of the original mixture.

A pot-pourri can be based entirely on bought petal mixtures, adding spices and essences of your own choice – or you can supply all the ingredients yourself. Use a measuring jug for gauging quantities.

Rose Pot-Pourris

Rose and Lavender Pot-Pourri
2 pts (1 litre) rose petals of any shade
½ pt (¼ litre) lavender flowers
1 pt (½ litre) mint leaves
1 tablespoon orris root powder
1 grated nutmeg
few drops of rose oil and slightly less of
lavender oil

Rose and Carnation Pot-Pourri
1 pt (½ litre) rose petals
1 pt (½ litre) carnations or pinks, whole heads dried if possible
½ pt (¼ litre) rose-scented geranium leaves
1 tablespoon orris root powder
1 teaspoon powdered cloves and 1 tablespoon broken cloves
a few drops of rose and carnation oil

Summery Mixture
2 pts (1 litre) marigold flower heads
1 pt (½ litre) rose petals
½ pt (¼ litre) delphiniums or cornflowers
½ pt (¼ litre) nasturtium flowers
1 tablespoon lemon thyme
1 tablespoon dried and crushed orange peel
1 tablespoon orris root powder
few drops bergamot oil and few drops rose oil

Combine any number of flowers and leaves, be they from the garden or hedgerow. You can mix all the scented geranium-leaf varieties, adding small amounts of rose petals and rose oil to complement the rose-scented leaves; crushed and powdered citrus peel to complement any of the citrus fragrances; and a little nutmeg grated to echo nutmeg-scented leaves. Geranium flowers of any sort may be added.

A hedgerow pot-pourri could combine honeysuckle, clover, poppies, wild roses, rose-hips, woodruff, cranesbill, corn marigolds, etc. However, take the utmost care when picking flowers from a hedgerow. Pick only where there are plenty of flowers. Many species are endangered by indiscriminate picking. If you have room, let some of these wild flowers take up residence in your garden.

Think of special colours and fragrances combined together. A bowl full of creamy-coloured rose petals and some whole rose heads of the same colour combined with the aroma from vanilla pods is delicious.

Spicy mixtures can be made by mixing lavender, rosemary, thyme (plain and lemon), marjoram, sage (plain and 'pineapply' sage), peppermint, spearmint, apple mint, orange mint, eau-de-cologne mint, basil, hyssop, lemon balm, lemon verbena, geranium leaves, carnations, and rosebuds for colour, dried and powdered orange rind, a few crushed cloves, a little allspice, cinnamon, crushed gum benzoin and/or orris root powder.

Items for Pot-Pourri

Flowers for Colour and Shape Daisies, camomile, marigolds, nasturtiums, forget-me-nots, cornflowers, borage, chicory, flax (linium) in blue or red, delphiniums, hollyhocks, pansies, cranesbill, campanula, salvias, red valerian, peonies.

Fragrant Flowers Roses, lavender, stocks, wallflowers, honeysuckle, philadelphus (mock orange), heliotrope, violets, carnations and pinks, lilac, jasmine, lily of the valley, sweet williams, sweet peas, jonquil, narcissus and wistaria.

Fragrant Leaves Lavender, rosemary, scented geraniums, lemon balm, lemon verbena, mint varieties, basil, hyssop, marjoram, thyme varieties, sage varieties, eucalyptus, bay, lovage, tarragon, woodruff, sweet cicely and dill.

Fixatives Orris root, gum benzoin, costmary, sandalwood.

Spices and Aromatics Ginger, cinnamon, cloves, nutmeg, mace, coriander, cardamum, allspice, anise, caraway, cinnamon sticks, vanilla pods, juniper berries, dried and powdered citrus peel, cedarwood and sandalwood chips.

Oils Ready-blended pot-pourri oil, carnation, musk, musk rose, rose geranium, rose, violet, patchouli, lemon verbena, lavender, bergamot, orange, lemon, jasmine, hyacinth, lilac, marigold, heliotrope, camomile, honeysuckle, sweet-pea, gardenia, rosemary, lily of the valley, wallflower, etc.

Presenting Pot-Pourri

Gifts of pot-pourris can be presented in all manner of containers. Look out for old jars, ceramic or glass, stoppered or unstoppered, old tins, small wooden boxes, old cups, saucers and bowls, small jugs, and little dressing-table sets. Pot-pourri displayed in a flat shallow uncovered vessel will gradually lose some of its fragrance. If you have a mixture that is very pungent but you do not wish the fragrance to escape too quickly, or if the mixture is rather dull in appearance, use old pomanders (pierced pots especialy for pot-pourri) or look for sugar-sifter pots with pierced tops.

You might find someone who is keen to make simple pottery

containers as the start of a small business venture. The humblest items, such as clean terracotta flowerpots, make good containers. You can hand-paint vessels with enamel paints. If a vessel has no lid, cling-film makes a good, functional covering while your pot-pourri is in transit.

Clove Oranges

A clove-studded orange is a traditional pomander. It can be hung in a wardrobe or in a room to impart a warm, spicy aroma, particularly pleasant for Christmas time. Patience will be needed to make a successful clove orange.

Take an orange which is a good shape and free from blemishes. Try to find the best quality cloves you can. The best ones come from Zanzibar and have large heads. Avoid very small, brittle-headed cloves. Gently roll the orange around in your hands to warm and soften the skin, then stick the cloves into the skin as evenly as possible, leaving one head's width between each to allow for shinkage. This shrinkage room is essential to allow the centre of the orange to dry out properly. If the orange skin is very hard and tough, pierce the skin gently with the point of a fine knitting needle before attempting to insert the cloves.

Make up a powder mixture of ground orris root, cinnamon and clove. Place the cloved orange gently on a piece of greaseproof paper and gently sift on the powder. Roll the orange around in the surplus powder until all of it has been thoroughly dusted. Then dry it very slowly, if possible in a warm and airy place such as an airing cupboard. Humidity will cause mildew and too fierce a heat will dry the outside to brittleness, leaving the centre soft and prone to rot. This drying may take several weeks. You may spray or paint on an aromatic oil, such as oil of clove and orange to enhance the aroma. A little extra drying time will be required. Put a circle of ribbon around the finished pomander (it may be easier if you leave an area free of cloves to take the ribbon) making a loop for hanging. A lemon can be used instead of an orange.

Sachets

Small sachets of fragrant herbs can be used to perfume clothes in drawers and wardrobes and hung on coathangers. Not only do they make the clothes fragrant, but they also help to keep insects away, especially moths which damage woollens. This method is far more pleasant than mothballs! Experiment with any of the pot-pourri mixtures. If you use certain oily crushed spices such as nutmeg and cloves or added oils, make sure that these are well-blended and left to 'air' before use. Oily, dusty particles can stain fine fabrics if allowed to escape from the sachet through seams or open weaves.

Rose petals combined with scented-leaf geraniums make a good mixture to keep clothes sweet. A little rose geranium and/or lemon verbena oil may be added. Lavender may be used on its own or combined with rosemary and lemon verbena leaves.

Lemon verbena, combined with powdered lemon and orange peel, a little powdered orris root and a few drops of bergamot oil is refreshing, particularly for those who do not like flowery, sweet fragrances.

You need not spend vast amounts of money on fabrics and trimmings to make sachets. If you detest sewing you can put non-oily mixtures into plain coloured envelopes and seal them. The plainest of fabrics can be embellished by embroidering or cutting out motifs from other fabrics and sewing them on. Most shops sell more expensive cotton lawns – Liberty-type fabrics – in 3 in (10 cm) strips. Otherwise look out for remnants of attractive cottons, including plain colours, floral prints, stripes and ginghams. Jumble sales can be a good source of attractive old cotton dresses which can be cut up as needed. Similarly, cotton sheets, pieces of lace and even old silks and linens sometimes turn up at sales. Large bundles often come up for auction – you may find some very good bits and pieces in this way. Save scraps of ribbon and any odds and ends for your work basket.

Air Fresheners and Insect Repellents

Any pot-pourri mixture makes a good air freshener. Combine any of the following herbs in muslin or hessian bags, and hang about the house to deter flies and insects: lavender, sweet woodruff, lemon verbena, star anise, costmary, tansy, any of the mints – the more the better, thyme, rosemary, bay, camomile, basil.

Bunches of lavender, tansy and mint can be tied together and hung in the kitchen, especially near doors and windows, where they should help to deter flies.

In the Kitchen

Put sachets with cinnamon sticks, vanilla pods, nutmegs, etc. into drawers and cupboards. If you keep all your herbs and spices for cooking in a small enclosed cupboard, especially a wooden cupboard, you will soon notice the delicious aroma that permeates it.

Lemon Thyme and Lemon Verbena smell good if they are included in the wadding of an oven glove. The contact with heat, and the movement of the hand, will release the aroma every time the glove is used.

Sprigs of Dried Herbs can be placed between sheets and pillowcases in the airing cupboard.

Drawer-lining Paper can be made by filling the base of a very large, lidded box with a fragrant pot-pourri mixture. Make sure it is not oily. Lay sheets of patterned wrapping paper or small pieces of pretty wallpaper on top of it. You can use plain drawer-lining paper, available from old-fashioned hardware and household goods stores, and even paint on your own design. Turn the sheets over occasionally. Before long they will have absorbed the pot-pourri fragrance.

Similarly, writing paper and envelopes can be fragranced with pot-pourri. Once more, make sure that the pot-pourri is not oily.

Hot water-bottle covers can be made more pleasant by making a thin cover with a little pot-pourri in amongst the wadding – it will help to disguise the 'rubbery' smell!

Twigs of woody herbs, such as lavender, rosemary and lemon verbena may be thrown onto an open fire to make the smoke pleasantly aromatic.

Before switching on a table lamp, paint a little essential oil onto the top of the light bulb. When it is switched on, the heat will make the fragrance rise into the atmosphere.

Perfume Oils and Essences

To extract one ounce of rose essence would require thousands upon thousands of rose petals. This explains the great cost of absolutely neat plant extracts. You can try floating flowers on pure springwater in the sun and scooping of the oil that comes to the surface with cotton-wool buds. However, you cannot always get the spring water and the sunshine, and you may have to scoop off dust, insects and other bits and pieces.

Enfleurage Method

Cover a sheet of glass with a white vegetable fat, then press a layer of freshly-picked flowers into it. Leave for twenty-four hours. Remove the first layer and replace them with a fresh layer of flowers, again leaving for twenty-four hours. Repeat the process until the fat has taken on the fragrance of the flowers. It should take about a week. During the process keep the sheet of glass in a warm, dry place. When you have removed the last layer of flowers, scrape the fat into a container. It pays not to take too much of this at a time, because adding the few drops of tincture of benzoin you may need as a preservative can sometimes change the fragrance of your original product.

Jasmine and honeysuckle lend themselves well to this method of extraction. You can use this scented fat to add in small quantities to creams, or you can, if you have patience, make 'cologne'.

Take four times the weight of your scented fat in vodka (for example ½ oz (15 g) scented fat to 2 oz (60 g) *weight* of vodka). Put them in a screw-top jar together and leave in a cool, dark place. After several months skim the fat from the surface. In this time the alcohol will have absorbed the essential plant oil from the fat. Dilute the alcohol with water to make a scented cologne.

Oil Extraction

Take several handfuls of fresh flowers or leaves and press them firmly into a glass jar. Pour on warmed sunflower oil, screw on the lid and leave in a warm, sunny place for a week. Strain the oil off, re-pack the jar with more fresh flowers and leaves, re-warm the oil and pour over the new herbs. Repeat this process for as long as you need to reach the correct fragrance. This could be several weeks to a few months, depending on the strength you require.

These oils can be used to fragrance other mixtures, or as perfumes, and are ideal for massage. Add a few drops of tincture of benzoin to preserve, if desired, although the addition of some wheatgerm oil, which has preservative properties, may be preferred.

HERB STOCKISTS

Herb Farms

Ashfields Herb Nursery, Hinstock, Market Drayton, Salop TF9 2NG Tel. Sambrook 392 Plants and seeds, Catalogue
Bowling Alley Farm, Commonside, Alvanlay, Nr. Helsby, Cheshire
Candlesby Herbs, Cross Keys Cottage, Candlesby, Spilsby, Lincolnshire
Cornish Herbs, at Trelowarren, Trelow Cottage, Mawgan-in-Meneage, nr. Helston, Cornwall Tel. Mawgan 374
The Cottage Herbery, Mill House, Boraston Ford, Boraston, Nr. Tenbury Wells, Worcestershire Tel. Newnham Bridge 575 S.A.E. for free list
Culpeper Herb Farm, Floriston Hall, Wixoe, Halstead, Essex CO9 4AR Tel. (044085) 228 S.A.E. for free list
Daphne ffiske Herbs, Rosemary Cottage, Bramerton, Norwich NR14 7DW Tel. Surlingham 8187
Dorset Organic Herbs, Cherry Bank, Cheselbourne, Dorset DT2 7NT Tel. 025887 275
Eden Plants, Rossinver, Co. Leitrim, Eire Organically grown herbs. S.A.E. catalogue
Elidyr Nursery, Coleg Flidyr, Rhandirmwyn, Llandovery, Dyfed
Elly Hill Herbs, Elly Hill House, Barmpton, Darlington, Co. Durham DL1 3JF Tel. (0325) 464682
Foliage Scented and Herb Plants, Walton Poor Cottage, Ranmore, Dorking, Surrey. Tel. East Horsley 2273. Open Weds. Sats. and Sundays.

Fold Garden (Herbs and Succulent Plants), 26 Fold Lane, Biddulph, Staffs. ST8 7SG Tel. (0782) 513028 Visits appointment only day and evening. Mail order.

Heches Herbs, St Peter-in-the-Wood, Channel Islands. Tel. 0481 63545 Lecture holidays.

Hereford Herbs Ltd., Ocle Pychard, Herefordshire Tel. (0432) 78379

Nordybank Nurseries, Clee St Margaret, Craven Arms, Shrops Tel. Stock St Milborough 322 Herbs and wild flowers.

Herbs in Stock, Whites Hill, Stock, Essex. Tel. 0277-841130

The Herb Farm, Ivegill, Carlisle Tel. Southwaite 243

Herb Garden at Spots Farm, Small Hythe, Kent. Tel. 05806-3033

The Herb Garden, Hall View Cottage, Hardstoft, Pilsley, Nr. Chesterfield, Derbyshire Tel. (0246) 854268

Hollington Nurseries Ltd., Woolton Hill, Newbury, Berks. Tel. Highclere (0635) 253908 Discount available to personal callers only

Holywell Herbs, Holywell Hall, Brancepeth, Durham Tel. 0385 780245

Iden Croft Herb Farm, Frittenden Road, Staplehurst, Kent Tel. 0580-891432 Culinary and aromatic herbs. Herb shop and gardens.

Lathbury Park Herb Gardens, Newport Pagnell, Bucks Tel. Newport Pagnell 610316

Marle Place Plants, Marle Place, Brenchley, Tonbridge, Kent TN12 7HS Tel. (089272) 2304

Netherfield Herbs, 37 Nether Street, Rougham, Suffolk Tel. 0359 70452 Poster catalogue for three 2nd class stamps.

Norfolk Lavender Ltd., Caley Mill, Heacham, King's Lynn, Norfolk PE31 7JE Tel. Heacham 70384

Oak Cottage Herb Farm, Nesscliffe, Shropshire Tel. Nesscliffe 262

Old Rectory Herb Garden, Ightham, Sevenoaks, Kent Tel. Borough Green 882608

Parkinson Herbs, Barras Moor Farm, Perran ar Worthal, Truro, Cornwall Tel. Devoran 864380

Ravenshead Herbs, 7 Vernon Avenue, Ravenshead, Nottingham NG15 9BJ Tel. Mansfield (0623) 792957 Visits appointment only. Mail order.

Samares Herbs à Plenty, Samares Manor, St Clement, Jersey, Chanel Islands. Tel (0534) 79635, 70551 Herb shop, herb gardens, herb nursery

Scotherbs, Waterybutts, Grange by Errol, Perthshire PH2 7SZ Tel. 082 12228 SAE for catalogue.

Selet Hall Herb Garden, Sellet Hall, Whittington, nr. Carnforth, Lancs Tel. 0468 71865

Selsley Herb and Goat Farm, Warerlane, Selsley, Stroud, Gloucestershire

Sifelle Herbs, Grafton Cottage, Isfield, Uckfield, Sussex Tel. Isfield (082575) 514

Springfields Herbs, Springfield, South Lane, Nether Stowey, Somerset TA5 1LR Tel. (0278) 732369

Stoke Lacy Herb Garden, Bromyard, Herefordshire. Plants, seeds, summer ½ day herb schools, open Thurs. and Sat., 2-5 pm

Suffolk Herbs, Sawyers Farm, Little Cornard, Sudbury, Suffolk Tel. 0787-227247 Herbs and a wide range of wild flower and herb seeds

The Weald Herbery, Park Cottage, Fritten, Cranbrook, Kent Tel. 058 080 226

Tippell, Mrs. J., 57 Ormesby Way, Kenton, Harrow, Middx Tel. 01-204-3663. Kingsbury Tube, Bakerloo Line. Variety of usual and unusual herbs.

Urban Herbs, 91 Clifton Road, Balsall Health, Birmingham B12 8SR Tel. 021-449-7236

Valeswood Herb Farm, Little Ness, Shropshire Tel. 0939 260376

Westhall Herbs, Aisling, Church Lane, Westhall, Nr. Halesworth, Suffolk IP19 8NU

Wilton Park Farm Market Garden, Old Beaconsfield, Bucks Tel. Beaconsfield 3418

Suppliers

Dried Herbs

Many health food shops and some herb farms carry a limited range of the more common herbs and spices. The following are able to supply between 50 and 200 varieties.

Baldwins, 173 Walworth Road, London, SE17 Tel. 01-703-5550 Tues. to Sats. 9 am – 5.30 pm. Closed Mondays. Mail order. S.A.E. for price list

Brews & Potions, 36 Steeley Lane, Chorley, Lancs Tel. Chorley 65100 Personal shoppers only

Cook's Delight, 360-362 High Street, Berkhamsted, Herts Tel. (04427) 3584

CULPEPER SHOPS

BATH 28 Milsom Street, Bath BA1 1DG Tel. (0223) 67370

BOURNEMOUTH 1 Post Office Road, Bournemouth Tel. (0202) 27107

BRIGHTON 12d Meeting House Lane, Brighton BN1 1HB Tel. (0273) 27939

CAMBRIDGE 25 Lion Yard, Cambridge CB2 3NA Tel. (0223) 67370

CANTERBURY 11 Marlowe Arcade, Canterbury CT1 2PT Tel (0227) 451121

CHESTER 24 Bridge Street, Chester CH1 1NQ Tel. (0244) 317774

GUILDFORD 10 Swan Lane, Guildford GU1 4EQ Tel. (0483) 60008

LINCOLN 4 The Corn Exchange Buildings, Cornhill, Lincoln LN5 7HH Tel. (0522) 45013

LIVERPOOL 1 Cavern Walks, Mathew Street, Liverpool L2 6RE Tel. 051-236-5780

LONDON 21 Bruton Street, Berkeley Square, London W1X 7DA Tel. 01-629-4559

LONDON 9 Flask Walk, Hampstead, London, NW3 1HJ Tel. 01-794-7263

LONDON No. 8 The Market, Covent Garden, London, WC2 Tel. 01-379-6698

NORWICH 14 Bridewell Alley, Norwich NR2 1AQ Tel. (0603) 618911

OXFORD 7 New Inn Hall Street, Oxford, OX1 2DH Tel. (0865) 249754

SALISBURY 33 High Street, Salisbury, SP1 2NJ Tel. (0722) 26159

WINCHESTER 4 Market Street, Winchester, SO23 8LS Tel. (0962) 52866

YORK 43 Low Petergate, York, YO1 2HT Tel. (0904) 51654

Dorwest Herb Growers, Shipton Gorge, Bridport, Dorset Tel. Burton Bradstock (0308) 897272

Down to Earth, Herbal Specialists 3 The Grove, Coulsdon, Surrey CR3 2BH Tel. 01-660-0425 Mail order only. S.A.E. for list.

Gerard House (1965) Ltd., 736 Christchurch Road, Boscombe, Bournemouth Tel. Bournemouth 35352

Hartwood Aromatics (HR) 12 Station Road, Hatton, Warwick CV35 7LG Tel. 0926 84 2873 Pure herbal essential oils

The Herb Shop, Riverside Place, 2 St James Street, Taunton, Somerset TA1 1JH Tel. (0823) 54900 Herbal products, herb garden design and courses

Laundry Farm Herbs, Nesscliffe, Shrewsbury, Shropshire SY1 AX Tel. Nesscliffe (074) 381 406

L'herboriste, 98 Addison Gardens, London W14 Tel. 01-603-5675

Market Shop, 48 Bridge Street, Berwick upon Tweed TD15 1AQ Wholefoods, herbs and spices

Neal's Yard Wholefood Warehouse, 20/23 Shorts Gardens, London WC2 Tel. 01-836-5151

Potters (Herbal Supplies) Ltd, Leyland Mill Lane, Wigan Tel. (0942) 34761 Herbal remedies

Sussex Herbs, 6 Cliffe Shopping Arcade, 34/36 Cliffe High Street, Lewes, East Sussex Tel. Lewes 4771125

Tullivers, 29 Goodramgate, York Tel. (0904) 36437

Welshpool Herbs and Spices, 24 High Street, Welshpool, Powys Tel. (0938) 3180

Wild Thymes, 37b Sydney Road, Richmond, Surrey TW9 1UB S.A.E. for price list.

Witch Wood, Oldfield Road, Bickley, Kent BR1 2LE. Mail order only—view and collection by arrangement. Please enclose S.A.E. for price list.

INDEX